Mantegna
to
Cézanne

Mantegna *to* Cézanne

Master Drawings from the Courtauld

A Fiftieth Anniversary Exhibition

William Bradford
and Helen Braham

Published for the Courtauld Institute Galleries
by British Museum Publications Ltd

© 1983 Home House Society Trustees
ISBN 0 7141 0796 4

Published for the Trustees of the Home House Society,
Courtauld Institute of Art, University of London,
by British Museum Publications Ltd, 46 Bloomsbury St,
London WC1B 3QQ

Designed by Harry Green

Printed in England by Balding + Mansell Limited, London & Wisbech

Contents

List of Colour Plates

Introduction

The present exhibition of 126 Master Drawings from the Courtauld Institute Galleries is one of three which have been organised to celebrate the fiftieth anniversary of the Courtauld Institute of Art, University of London. Although the actual foundation took place in 1931, it was not until October 1932 that the Institute admitted its first students at 20 Portman Square, which until recently had been the home of our principal benefactor, Samuel Courtauld. Thus we regard the current academic year 1982–83 as our fiftieth anniversary. We were delighted when the Trustees of the British Museum agreed to hold an exhibition to mark the occasion. We are very grateful to them and to our colleagues at the British Museum for their enthusiastic support, and not least to British Museum Publications Ltd for publishing an illustrated catalogue.

We thought it would be appropriate to try to show the richness and variety of our collections of drawings and watercolours, which though small in comparison with the holdings of the British Museum's Department of Prints and Drawings, nevertheless contain works of the finest quality.

The largest of our constituent collections, formed by Sir Robert Witt and bequeathed to us in 1952, was not chosen solely on the principle of quality or through a wish to specialise in a particular school. Given his relatively modest means, he decided to concentrate on obtaining representative work by artists, who, while interesting or charming, were slightly below the highest rank, or who were temporarily out of fashion. There are certainly works of great intrinsic beauty in the collection, but Sir Robert conceived his collection as supplementing the library of reproductions (which he also bequeathed to the Institute). These drawings are, in a sense, a corpus of documents of use to the art historian, and as such, could help the student to identify the characteristics of a large range of artists. The acquisition of a work signed by a rare artist always gave him particular pleasure. It is a reflection of the relative neglect of seventeenth-century Italian art in this country between the two world wars, that Sir Robert was able to acquire nineteen drawings by the Carracci brothers, six by Pietro da Cortona, and thirty-nine by Guercino (including thirty-three drawings from the Earl of Gainsborough's collection); as well as stage designs by the Bibiena family, Bigari, Piranesi, and Valeriani, of the eighteenth century. But, as one might expect, the British School forms the largest group of drawings. Here, there are over forty drawings and a group of fifty small figure studies by Gainsborough, some of superb quality; while of earlier periods there are examples of Isaac Oliver's delicate draughtsmanship (cat. no. 52), and of robust baroque splendours such as Lely's *Two Heralds* (cat. no. 48). The English landscape painters of the eighteenth and nineteenth centuries are well represented, and there are good examples by artists as diverse as Fuseli, Rowlandson, Wilkie, Burne-Jones and Whistler. The collection has been added to since Sir Robert's death, at first using money bequeathed by him, and more recently from visitors' donations.

But the great names of the English watercolour school were not systematically collected by Sir Robert Witt, and this weakness was made good in a most handsome way by the bequest of William Spooner and by his wife's gift in 1967. There are, in fact, three collections. The first consists of drawings acquired by Spooner before his marriage, which, with those collected by him and his wife from 1938–67, were bequeathed to the University of London, with a life interest in some cases to Mrs Spooner. Then there is a group of drawings and watercolours collected by Mrs Spooner and her first husband, H.B. Milling, who was a specialist in the subject, some of which have been included in the bequest. Others have been acquired specially by Mrs Spooner since 1967 with the intention of remedying weaknesses in the collection and these she has presented to us. The Spooner bequest and gift contains splendid watercolours by Cotman, Alexander and J.R. Cozens, Girtin, Sandby, and Francis Towne, some of which we have included in this exhibition.

One of our greatest artists, J.M.W. Turner, was only represented in both the Witt and Spooner collections by either comparatively slight works or at best unevenly. This deficiency was magnificently made good by the gift of thirteen Turner watercolours that had been collected by the late Sir Stephen Courtauld (brother of Samuel Courtauld), and which were given in his memory by the family in 1974. In May of that year they were shown for the first time as a group at the Courtauld Institute Galleries. Apart from six which were exhibited at Agnew's in 1951, these watercolours, once well-known, had become almost forgotten after Sir Stephen went to live in Rhodesia before the Second World War. They range from the earliest topographical work, *Chepstow Castle* of 1794 (cat. no. 120), to those executed during Turner's first visit to the Alps and immediately following it; next comes a group painted between 1816–30; then there are four late works of the 1840s which form a splendid coda to the whole. Two had belonged to Turner's lifelong friend and patron, Walter Fawkes, and three were once owned by John Ruskin.

The foundation collection of Impressionist and Post-Impressionist paintings, given or bequeathed by Samuel Courtauld, also contains watercolours, prints and drawings of roughly the same period. We have selected some of the finest of these, including three by Cézanne, two by Daumier, a Degas, and one each by Van Gogh, Manet, Rodin, Seurat, and Toulouse-Lautrec. These have been supplemented by five nineteenth-century drawings from the Princes Gate Collection.

Many of the chief glories of the earlier sections of the exhibition are provided by the Princes Gate Collection, bequeathed to us in 1978 by Count Antoine Seilern, and arguably one of the most munificent single Old Master benefactions to the nation of this century. The scope and quality of this collection was first revealed to the general public in July 1981, when almost all the paintings and a selection of drawings were exhibited at the Courtauld Institute Galleries. Now we have taken the opportunity provided by this exhibition to include over fifty drawings from the Princes Gate Collection, of which a sizeable proportion has not been shown before as a group. Count Seilern's activities as a scholar and collector have been discussed in some detail by Mrs Helen Braham in the *Princes Gate Collection* catalogue (1981), and there is probably little more to be said on this aspect save to rejoice that these precious drawings have been entrusted to us. It should also be mentioned that, under the terms of Count Seilern's will, we are prohibited from lending any of the drawings from his collection to exhibitions located outside London. During his lifetime, Count Seilern lent drawings to scholarly exhibitions further afield, but he evidently came to the conclusion that drawings in transit might be at greater risk than other objects, and we must respect the wishes of one of our great benefactors.

The catalogue has been compiled by William Bradford and Helen Braham under the editorship of Dr Dennis Farr. We are very grateful to Mr Bradford and Mrs Braham for working to a tight deadline. All the drawings have been physically examined and some new information has come to light which has been incorporated, especially for Witt and Spooner drawings, but details concerning provenance have generally been omitted unless the drawing concerned has belonged at some stage to a well-known collector. Bibliographical references have also been kept to an essential minimum, although the reader is referred to the seven-volume catalogue of the Princes Gate collection compiled by Count Seilern (under the appropriate inventory number), or to the recent Princes Gate catalogue (1981) to which reference is made at the end of those entries for drawings which were recently shown at the Courtauld Institute Galleries. The entries for the Turner watercolours are based on those written by Professor Michael Kitson for the 1974 exhibition, and we are grateful to Dr David Freedberg for his help over the interpretation of the inscription on the Stradanus *Pearl-diving* (cat. no. 35).

We wish to thank Dr David Wilson, Director of the British Museum, and Mr Michael Hoare and his colleagues of British Museum Publications Ltd who cheerfully undertook the production of this catalogue at short notice; and we are indebted to Miss Jean Rankine, Mr Gordon Barber, the design staff and technicians at the British Museum, as well as to Mr John Rowlands, for all their help in this enterprise. We thank Mr Gordon and Mr Simon Roberton, of A.C. Cooper Ltd, Mr William Clarke, Miss Kirsty Fergusson, Miss Robin Featherstone, and our colleagues in the Photographic Department of the Courtauld for their assistance.

PETER LASKO	DENNIS FARR
Director	*Director*
Courtauld Institute of Art	Courtauld Institute Galleries *December 1982*

The Fifteenth Century

Giovanni Bellini (c.1430–1516)

1 *The Nativity* COLOUR PLATE I

Pen and different shades of ink, slightly washed; both upper corners cut. *c.*20.1 × 21.2 cm.
Inscribed in ink by a later hand, bottom right: 'L.' Collector's marks: Lely (twice); various numerals on *verso* and mount.

PRINCES GATE COLLECTION 79

One of the few surviving composition studies by Bellini, dating from *c.*1475. The use of the broken pen line was apparently his invention. The predella of Bellini's *Pesaro Altarpiece* (Museo Civico) of about the same date shows the same subject with certain general similarities. (Princes Gate Catalogue 125)

Albrecht Dürer (1471–1528)

2 *The Emperors Charlemagne and Sigismund*
COLOUR PLATE II

Pen and ink and watercolour. The sheet folded down centre to indicate wings of diptych. 17.7 × 20.6 cm.
On the left, Charlemagne's heraldic devices, the two-headed eagle and fleurs-de-lys; on the right, the Imperial two-headed eagle above Sigismund, flanked by blank shields inscribed by the artist (brackets here denote corrections in darker ink, probably by a later hand): '(H)ongern'; '(B)eheim'; 'daltz' ('Dalmatien'); 'crobatz' ('Croatien').

PRINCES GATE COLLECTION 253

This watercolour, from the Imhoff and Lubomirski collections, is a preparatory study for the two large paintings of the emperors (Nuremberg, Germanisches Museum), commissioned from Dürer 1510 and completed 1513 with numerous differences from the watercolour and no longer forming a diptych as projected here. They were intended for the 'Heiltumskammer', where the Imperial Insignia of the Holy Roman Empire were preserved. (Princes Gate Catalogue 163)

Albrecht Dürer (1471–1528)

3 *One of the Wise Virgins*

Pen and ink. 29 × 20 cm.
Inscribed in a later hand, top centre, with the (wrong) date: '1508', and 'A.D.', and bottom left: '9'. Dated by the artist, on *verso*, top centre: '1493'. Collector's mark: Lawrence.
Verso: Two Studies of a Man's left Leg, pen and ink.

PRINCES GATE COLLECTION 251

This is among the most outstanding drawings of Dürer's *Wanderjahre* (1490–94). For part of 1493, the year of this sheet, he was in Strasbourg; he had been to Colmar, hoping to meet Martin Schongauer, who had, however, just died. The source of Dürer's drawing may have been a lost project by Schongauer, whose influence is evident, for a series of the Wise and Foolish Virgins. (Princes Gate Catalogue 161)

Albrecht Dürer (1471–1528)

4 *Studies of Two Horsemen*

Brush and ink; pen(?) with a darker shade of ink; wash. Scribbles in ink at top centre, and two wavy lines in grey ink, bottom left. Evidently a fragment. Laid down. 13 × 12.1 cm. Collector's mark: Skippe.

PRINCES GATE COLLECTION 252

This fragment may have belonged, with *The Virgin with S. John and the Weeping Women* (British Museum), to a composition of a Calvary scene. Both are in the same technique, unusual for Dürer, drawn with the tip of the brush, not pen; their authenticity has been doubted on these grounds, but they are almost certainly autograph, of *c.*1493–4. (Princes Gate Catalogue 162)

Leonardo da Vinci *(1452–1519)*

5 *Studies for a S.Mary Magdalene*

Pen and ink. 13.9 × 7.9 cm.
Collector's mark: Lawrence.

PRINCES GATE COLLECTION 80

All the artist's framing lines are visible, but this sheet is evidently a fragment. The subject of these studies cannot be connected with any known work by Leonardo, although the pose of the upper figure suggests comparison with the portrait of *Cecilia Gallerani* (Cracow). The drawing, formerly in the Fenwick Collection, has been dated to *c*.1480. (Princes Gate Catalogue 169)

Andrea Mantegna *(1431–1506)*

6 *Studies for Christ at the Column*

Pen and ink. 23.6 × 14.4 cm.
Collector's mark: Skippe.
Verso: Studies for Christ at the Column, pen and ink.

PRINCES GATE COLLECTION 345

Both *recto* and *verso* show studies for a *Flagellation* by Mantegna, known through two fifteenth-century engravings, which must record a lost painting or finished drawing, perhaps part of an unfinished series of Passion scenes. The publication in 1930 of the *recto* (*verso* not uncovered until 1958) aroused the long controversy over the attribution of drawings to Mantegna or Bellini. Acquired as a Bellini, this is now assigned to Mantegna, *c*.1460, or earlier. (Princes Gate Catalogue 170)

Bernardino Pinturicchio(?) *(c.1454–1513)*

7 *Study of a Flying Angel*

Metalpoint, pen (and brush) and ink, heightened with white bodycolour, on prepared grey ground. 21.7 × 13.9 cm.
Collectors' marks: Lawrence (*verso*); Mayor; Heseltine (*verso*).
Verso: A Standing Man, seen from the Back, in a similar technique.

PRINCES GATE COLLECTION 81

Both sides of the sheet record figures in Pêrugino's Sistine Chapel frescoes (completed 1482) and both recur in the work of his assistant, Pinturicchio, who probably made these as copies for later use. *The Flying Angel* derives from the fresco destroyed to make way for Michelangelo's *Last Judgement* and appears in Pinturicchio's *Glory of S.Bernardino* in S.Maria d'Aracoeli in Rome (1484). The sheet has also been ascribed to Giovanni Santi. (Princes Gate Catalogue 176)

1

2

3

4

5

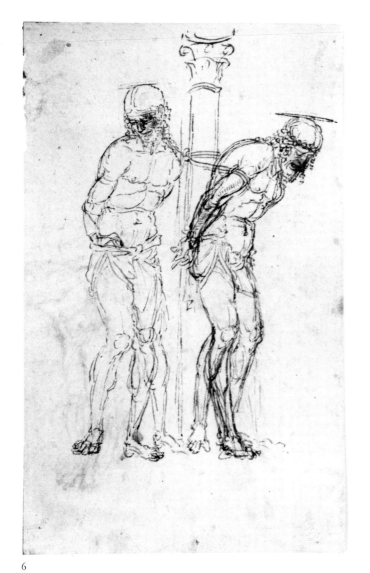

6

7

The Sixteenth Century

Federigo Baroccio *(1526–1612)*

8 *Study of a Bending Man*

Black chalk, with the use of rubbing or the stump, and red chalk; on blue (now unevenly discoloured and stained) laid paper. The sheet unevenly trimmed at all sides. 33.3 × 22.4 cm. Inscribed in different hands in pencil, lower left: 'H'(?), and: 'F Baroccio', and in black chalk, *verso*: 'Barroccio'.
Verso: Slight Study of a Bending Man, and a Drapery Study, in black chalk heightened with white chalk.
Collector's mark: Wiesböck (inscription, *verso*); Habich.

WITT COLLECTION 2329

The drawing on the *recto* is one of four studies for the doctor in the painting *The Circumcision*, signed and dated 1590, commissioned by the Compagnia del Nome di Dio for the Church of Nome di Gesù, Pesaro (now in the Louvre). Two studies for this figure – a nude study and a drapery study – are in the Kupferstichkabinett, Berlin (Harald Olsen, *Federico Barocci*, Copenhagen, 1962, under no.43), while the fourth study, a slight sketch underlying the drawing on the *verso* of the present sheet, is unknown to Olsen. It is possible that the indented contours of a nude figure, which underlie and form the basis of the figure on the *recto* of the Witt sheet, were pressed through from the nude study in Berlin, although this awaits confirmation.

The drapery study on the *verso* of the Witt sheet may be a preliminary drawing for the cloak of the Virgin Mary, also for *The Circumcision*: a similar hassock to that on which she kneels in the painting is included in the drawing.

Fra Bartolommeo della Porta *(1472–1517)*

9 *The Approach to a Mountain Village*

Pen and ink. 29.1 × *c*.20.6 cm. (bottom right corner missing)

PRINCES GATE COLLECTION 83

This and the four following drawings were, from 1730 to 1957, bound in an album made for F.M.N. Gabburri containing forty-one sheets of landscape and nature studies by Fra Bartolommeo, many drawn on both sides. Amongst the earliest of their kind, they probably all date after 1504 when the artist resumed his career as a painter at S.Marco in Florence. Although none has been directly connected with his known paintings, this drawing was used for Bugiardini's *Rape of Dina* (Vienna, Kunsthistorisches Museum), a painting apparently begun by Fra Bartolommeo.

Fra Bartolommeo della Porta *(1472–1517)*

10 *A Tree in Winter*

Pen and ink. 28.7 × 21.2 cm.

PRINCES GATE COLLECTION 84

From the album described under cat. no. 9 above. A number of similar studies of trees in winter were in the same album. (Princes Gate Catalogue 154)

Fra Bartolommeo della Porta *(1472–1517)*

11 *A Northern Village on the Wooded Banks of a Stream*

Pen and ink. 28.2 × 21.7 cm.
Verso: A Town on the Banks of a River, pen and ink.

PRINCES GATE COLLECTION 85

From the album described under cat. no. 9 above. The drawing is evidently inspired by a Northern work of art. The architectural details on the *verso* indicate a view in the Veneto, which would date the sheet to 1508 when Fra Bartolommeo visited Venice.

Fra Bartolommeo della Porta *(1472–1517)*

12 *A Path leading between overhanging Rocks*

Pen and ink. 21.4 × 28.7 cm.
Verso: Three Houses in a Mountain Village, pen and ink.

From the album described under cat. no. 9 above. Similar rocky landscapes can be seen on two other sheets from the album in the Princes Gate Collection (inv. nos. 87, 89), which are not on exhibition.

Fra Bartolommeo della Porta
(1472–1517)

13 *The Sweep of a River with Fishermen and a Town in the Background*

Pen and ink. 21.1 × 29 cm.

From the album described under cat. no. 9 above. (Princes Gate Catalogue 124)

Hans Bol *(1534–93)*

14 *The Bad Shepherd*

Traces of black chalk or pencil; pen and pale brown ink; blue watercolour wash, with some drawing with the point of the brush; on off-white laid paper. The pictorial area enclosed within a ruled line in pen and brown ink. The drawing pressed through for engraving, the *verso* of the sheet prepared with red chalk for transfer to the plate. The sheet unevenly trimmed at all sides. 20.5 × 20.5 cm.
Inscribed in pencil, bottom right: 'H.BOL' Traces of inscriptions, now illegible, but apparently by three different hands, in pen and brown ink, and pencil, *verso*, dated: '1576', and numbered: '12'.

The drawing, engraved by Peter van der Heyden (Hollstein III, p. 52, no. 203) is regarded by Franz (op. cit., no. 98) as the pendant to cat. no. 15. Although the sheets are of comparable size, their relationship formally, in terms of coherent symbolism, and of subject matter is loose. They were also drawn at different times (*cf.* inscribed date). The true pendant to the present sheet, a drawing which depicts the Good Shepherd and Saints repairing the sheep-fold, was also in the collection of Sir Robert Witt (exhibited: *Flemish and Belgian Art*, Royal Academy, 1927, no. 535). The imagery of the *Bad Shepherd* relies heavily on Pieter Bruegel's drawing *The Parable of the Good Shepherd*, no longer extant, but known from Philip Galle's engraving of 1565 (Lebeer, *op. cit.* no. 59). Unlike Bruegel, however, Bol sets the sheep-fold more naturalistically into the wider context of an extensive landscape, in which scenes of laziness, cowardice, and slaughter of sheep reinforce the drawing's main theme. Compositionally, the raised central motif contrasting with the broad, undulating background refers to landscape drawings made by Bol in the previous year, e.g. *Landscape with a Group of Trees.* (Rijksprentenkabinet, Amsterdam: Franz, no. 93)

Hans Bol *(1534–93)*

15 *The City of Jerusalem, with Christ as the Good Shepherd*

Traces of black chalk or graphite; pen and pale brown ink; blue watercolour wash; on off-white laid paper. The pictorial area enclosed within both ruled and free-hand lines in pen and brown ink. The drawing pressed through for engraving, the *verso* of the sheet prepared with red chalk for transfer to the plate. The sheet unevenly trimmed at all sides.
20.3 × 30.4 cm.
Signed in pen and brown ink, lower left; 'HANS BOL/1575'.

This drawing (H. Gerhard Franz, *Hans Bol als Landschaftszeichner*, Jahrbuch des Kunsthistorischen Institutes der Universität Graz, I, 1965, no. 97), was the subject of an engraving recorded by Hollstein (II, p. 54, no. 226). For its relationship with the previous drawing, see the note to cat. no. 14.
The geometrical layout of the ideal City of Jerusalem, a circular centre from which radiate straight avenues which are then intersected at right-angles by parallel avenues, is related to that of the garden shown in Bol's drawing of 1573 depicting one of the months (Spring?) (Kupferstichkabinett, Berlin: Franz no. 77).
As in the previous drawing, the scene is set in an extensive and relatively flat landscape, of a type with which Bol began to experiment at the end of the 1560s, possibly as a reaction against the mountainous and claustrophobic landscapes of the Biblical subjects he had executed in 1568. (*cf.* Franz nos. 44–50)

Paul Bril *(1554–1626)*

16 *Rocky Landscape*

Pencil; pen and brown ink, and dark brown ink restricted to the tree, right; on cream laid paper.
The sheet unevenly trimmed at all sides. 20.3 × 27.4 cm.
Signed in pen and brown ink, bottom centre: 'Pauuelse bril i607', and inscribed bottom right: 'Roma' (partly cut away).

WITT COLLECTION 1030

The sheet helps document the change of style which occurred in Bril's drawings and paintings during the first decade of the seventeenth century, when, under the influence of Adam Elsheimer, he moved away from his earlier mannerist handling to compose more classical landscape designs, made up of a limited number of clearly defined elements (*cf.* Giorgio T. Faggin, *Per Paolo Bril*, 'Paragone' no. 185/5, July 1965, p. 23).

The firm and vigorous draughtsmanship displayed in this drawing may have been influenced by engravings, particularly those after Domenico Campagnola.

A prominent motif in Bril's work of this period is the hilltop city or castle: it appears most spectacularly in the *Feudi di Casa Mattei* paintings of 1604 (four of which are now in the Palazzo Barberini, Rome), as well as in the Witt drawing, and sheets now in the Louvre. (F. Lugt, *Inventaire Général des Dessins des Ecoles du Nord Ecole Flamande*, Louvre, Paris, 1949, Vol. I, nos. 399 and 401)

Pieter Bruegel the Elder
(c.1525/30–69)

17 *Alpine Landscape*

Pen and ink in several shades of brown. 19.5 × 32.2 cm.
Collector's mark: Lawrence.

PRINCES GATE COLLECTION 10

Formerly thought to be the most advanced in this series of alpine landscapes (see cat. no. 21 below), this sheet has recently been placed amongst the earliest known. It was formerly in the Fenwick Collection.

Pieter Bruegel the Elder
(c.1525/30–69)

18 *An Alpine Landscape*

Pen and ink. Backed. 24.7 × 42.8 cm.
Inscribed, not by the artist: bottom left, 'P.bruegel 1547'; on the *verso* (backing), in nineteenth century(?) hand, in ink: 'Devon[re]', 'View on the Rhine Hemskirk'.

PRINCES GATE COLLECTION 315

The inscribed date cannot be correct; previously dated to *c.*1555, among the mature alpine views, this has now been placed between the earlier and later views, *c.*1552. (See also cat. no. 21 below)

Pieter Bruegel the Elder *(c.1525/30–69)*

19 *The Kermesse at Hoboken*

Slight traces of preliminary drawing in black chalk or graphite; pen and brown ink; on pale buff (now unevenly discoloured and stained) laid paper. The sheet rubbed in certain areas, and apparently folded roughly into quarters. The edges of the sheet trimmed, apparently to a graphite line (in part visible at top and bottom). The sheet pressed through for engraving. 26.5 × 39.4 cm.

LORD LEE OF FAREHAM COLLECTION 45

Dated and signed in pen and brown ink, lower left of centre: '1559/BRVEGEL' (the 'VE' in monogram).

Inscribed by the artist in pen and brown ink on the banner, left: '.../hoboken/.../kan(?)...'

The authenticity of this drawing has been questioned, without conclusive argument, by both Charles de Tolnay (*The Drawings of Pieter Bruegel the Elder*, London, 1952, A20), and Louis Lebeer (*Catalogue raisonné des estampes de Pierre Bruegel l'ancien*, Brussels, 1969, no. 30). Ludwig Münz (*Pieter Bruegel, The Drawings*, London, 1961, no. 141) confirms the attribution to Bruegel on the basis of the signature, whose form and style correspond with other examples by the artist dating from 1559 (e.g. those on the series of *Virtues*, Münz, 142–8).

The drawing was evidently popular, as it was engraved with additions and omissions in the reverse sense, by Frans Hogenberg(?) (Lebeer, *ibid.*), first published by Bartolomeus de Mompere, later by Ioannes Galle, and, finally, with much re-working of the shadows, in an edition inscribed: 'Susanna Verbruggen'. The extent to which the Lee sheet has been trimmed is evident when compared with the engraving, which includes at the top a view of treetops and sky. The lateral sides of the drawing have also been slightly trimmed (the engraving includes the complete barrel, on the right of the drawing, and three pitch-forks leaning against the wall of the house, on the left of the drawing), as has the bottom.

The drawing, as Walter Gibson has noted, (*Bruegel*, London, 1977, p. 159), is probably the first in Bruegel's oeuvre to explore the theme of peasant revelry at festivals, and was apparently followed by a similar design, *The Kermesse of S. George*, known from the engraving by H. Cock (published *c*.1561), in which the eye is led through the composition by a series of interlinked diagonals and curves.

Pieter Bruegel the Elder
(c.1525/30–69)

20 *Landscape with an Artist sketching*

Pen and ink in several shades of brown with faint traces of black chalk. 27.2 × 39.7 cm.
Inscribed in ink in sixteenth-century(?) hand, lower left: 'de ouden Breugel'; on the *verso*, in pencil: 'den ouden Breugel no. 56'.

PRINCES GATE COLLECTION 9

This alpine landscape was formerly thought to show a development in style from cat. no. 21 below now the reverse has been proposed. Both sheets may have belonged to the sixteenth-century artist, Georg Hoefnagel, and both were bound in the same album from *c*.1800–*c*.1948. (Princes Gate Catalogue 126)

Pieter Bruegel the Elder
(c.1525/30–69)

21 *Landscape with Two Mules*

Pen and ink in several shades of brown. 29.4 × 42.6 cm.
Traces of an inscription(?), bottom left; numerals on *verso*.

PRINCES GATE COLLECTION 8

Bruegel's alpine landscape drawings (see also cat. nos. 17, 18, 20 above) resulted from travels through the Alps on his Italian journey, *c*.1551–54/5. Very few are of identifiable places, being generally composed from motifs, some of which appear in more than one drawing, and in a series of landscape engravings made after his return to the Netherlands. The date and order of these alpine views are debatable, a recent theory being that the more naturalistic views preceded the more artificial *Weltlandschaft* panoramas with their different pen-style, such as this one, instead of the reverse development, and that all are earlier than previously supposed, the early instead of the mid-1550s.

Pieter Bruegel the Elder
(c.1525/30–69)

22 *View of Antwerp from the Sea*

Pen and ink in several shades of brown, faint traces of black chalk. Laid down. 20.3 × 29.9 cm.
Inscribed, not by the artist, bottom left: 'Breughel'.

PRINCES GATE COLLECTION 11

Dated to *c*.1559, this drawing is thought to be some years later than the alpine landscapes. It is possible that the city of Antwerp is portrayed allegorically: the ships appear to be sailing from sunshine into storm and the tiny island in the foreground is occupied only by the gallows. (Princes Gate Catalogue 127)

Antonio Allegri, *called* Correggio
(1489/94–1534)

23 *Christ in 'The Coronation of the Virgin'*

Red chalk over faint traces of black chalk; squared in red
chalk. Laid down. 16 × 13.4 cm.
Inscribed in Richardson's hand, on the mount: 'Coreggio';
in ink on the back, his shelf numbers, some deleted.
Collectors' marks: Richardson Snr; Spencer.

PRINCES GATE COLLECTION 352

This study is for the figure of Christ in the fresco formerly
decorating the apse of S. Giovanni Evangelista, Parma; a
fragment of the original is in the Galleria Nazionale, Parma,
and a copy in the present apse. The drawing appears to belong
early in the sequence of the seven known studies for this figure,
which probably date from 1522, although a recent theory that
Correggio painted the frescoes in the apse before those in the
cupola would suggest the date *c.*1520 for the drawing.

Hendrick Goltzius *(1558–1617)*

24 *The Prophetess Huldah*

Traces of preliminary drawing in black chalk or graphite;
pen and brown ink; brown and grey ink washes of varying
strengths and combinations, with drawing with the brush; a
slight touch of off-white bodycolour on the sleeve of the
cloak, left; some slight rubbing for the lights on the left
hand; on coarse pale buff (now stained) laid paper, prepared
by the artist with an uneven ground of pale grey (ink?) wash.
The pictorial area enclosed within a ruled line in pen and
brown ink, the sheet unevenly trimmed at all sides.
The drawing pressed through for engraving. 24 × 15.4 cm.
Signed in pen and brown ink, bottom left: 'HG' (in
monogram), and inscribed in pen and dark brown ink,
bottom left: 'hGo'. Vestiges of an erased inscription in pen
and dark brown ink, bottom right.
Inscribed in a modern hand in pencil, *verso*: 'Henry Goltzius',
and numbered 'P.46', and in pen and brown ink: '10.6', and
in red chalk: '2'.
Collector's mark: W. Young Ottley

WITT COLLECTION 2673

The drawing of the Prophetess Huldah, wife of Shallum (*cf.*
II Kings, XXII, 14–20), was engraved by J. Matham in 1588 as
one of the three plates from a series of *Prophetesses of the
Old Testament*. The other prophetesses were Jahel (wrongly
identified as Deborah) and Anna (*cf.* Hollstein, VIII, p. 132,
nos. 233–5, and E.J.K. Reznicek, *Die Zeichnungen von Hendrick
Goltzius*, Utrecht, 1961, K.23, K.16). A companion series of
Prophets from the Old Testament was also engraved by Matham
after Goltzius in 1589 (Hollstein, VIII, p. 132, nos. 228–32).
The present drawing has been related by Reznicek (*ibid.*) to
Goltzius' drawing of *Patientia*, of approximately the same date
(*cf.* Reznicek, no. K.97).

Martijn van Heemskerk *(1498–1574)*

25 *The Colossus at Rhodes*

Traces of preliminary drawing in black chalk; pen and
brown ink; on off-white (now unevenly stained) laid paper.
The pictorial area enclosed within a freehand line in pen and
brown ink, a ruled line in pen and dark brown ink
surrounding this by a later hand.
The drawing pressed through for engraving.
The sheet unevenly trimmed at all sides. 20.4 × 26.3 cm.
Signed in pen and brown ink, bottom left: 'Martijn van
Heemskerk/inventor', numbered bottom right of centre: '5',
and dated, right: '1570'.
Inscribed by the artist in pen and brown ink, top left: '5.
Colossus Solis'.

WITT COLLECTION 648

See notes to cat. no. 26.

Martijn van Heemskerk *(1498–1574)*

26 *The Temple of Diana at Ephesus*

Traces of preliminary drawing in black chalk; pen and
brown ink; on off-white (now unevenly stained) laid paper.
The pictorial area enclosed within a freehand line in pen and
brown ink, a ruled line in pen and dark brown ink
surrounding this by a later hand.

The drawing pressed through for engraving, the *verso* of the sheet prepared with black chalk for transfer to the plate. The sheet unevenly trimmed at all sides. 20.2 × 26.8 cm.
Signed in pen and brown ink, lower left: 'Heemskerk/inventor/1570', and numbered, bottom, right of centre: '4'.
Inscribed by the artist in pen and brown ink, top left: '4. Dianae Ephesiae Templum'.
Collector's marks: J.P.Zoomer.

WITT COLLECTION 647

This and the previous sheet are two preparatory drawings for the series of engravings *Octo Mundi Miracula* ('The Eight Wonders of the World') engraved by Philip Galle and published in an undated edition by Ioannes Galle (Hollstein, VIII, p. 245, nos. 357–64). Two other drawings for the same series, also signed and dated 1570 which represent the *Walls of Babylon*, and the eighth wonder of the world, *The Colosseum at Rome*, are in the Louvre (*cf.* Lise Duclaux, *Dessins de Martin van Heemskerk*, 'La revue du Louvre', December 1981). The remaining four drawings are as yet unlocated.

The numbering of the prints (which occurred in the second of three states, *cf.* Hollstein, *ibid.*) ignores Heemskerk's numbering, except in the case of number 8, the *Colosseum at Rome*.

The two drawings, faithfully reproduced in reverse in the engravings, set each of the wonders of the world into a mountainous landscape in which there is an imaginary view of the cities of Ephesus and Rhodes.

Lorenzo Lotto *(c.1480–1556)*

27 *Portrait of a Young Man*

Black chalk, slightly washed or rubbed in the cap, heightened with white and with red on the lips, on green prepared ground. 33.5 × 26.7 cm.
Collector's mark: Russell.

PRINCES GATE COLLECTION 90

The attribution to Lotto of this fine portrait drawing has generally been accepted without reservation, the only queries arising from the lack of comparable drawings by the artist. It appears to be related to Lotto's early painted portraits of *c.*1508–10. (Princes Gate Catalogue 137)

Michelangelo *(1475–1564)*

28 *Christ before Pilate*, or *S.Lawrence brought before the Prefect*

Pen and ink over some red chalk. 21 × 28.2 cm.
Inscribed in ink, bottom right: '2'.
Collectors' marks: Mariette; Witt (on mount).
Verso: parts of two unfinished sonnets by Michelangelo, studies of a leg, a torso and a head in red chalk and a pen-and-ink sketch of a slave, perhaps for the tomb of Julius II. At top of *recto* also a study for a leg.

PRINCES GATE COLLECTION 422

Michelangelo's authorship of the *recto* of this sheet has, unlike that of the *verso*, been doubted in the past but is now generally accepted. The *recto* may be connected with the commission of 1516 for the unexecuted façade of S.Lorenzo in Florence. The design suggests relief sculpture and the context would suggest that the subject shown may be *S.Lawrence brought before the Prefect*, rather than *Christ before Pilate*. (Princes Gate Catalogue 171)

Michelangelo *(1475–1564)*

29 *Christ on the Cross*

Black chalk. 30 × 18.7 cm.
Inscribed in ink, in late eighteenth or early nineteenth-century hand, bottom left: 'Michelange'; in an older hand, in centre of *verso*: 'n.° 16'.

PRINCES GATE COLLECTION 426

This belongs with a series of drawings of Christ on the Cross, dating from Michelangelo's last years, and all of an almost mystical intensity; in the others the Cross is flanked by the Virgin and S.John The drawings are characterised technically by a ruled crucifix, and by frequent alterations and repetitions of outline in the figures. Their purpose is not known, but may have been for presentation to friends, or as studies for a projected but unexecuted sculptural group. There is a copy at Frankfurt (Städelsches Kunstinstitut). (Princes Gate Catalogue 172)

Michelangelo *(1475–1564)*

30 *'The Dream of Human Life'*

Black chalk, stippled. Laid down. 39.6 × 27.8 cm.

PRINCES GATE COLLECTION 424

There are numerous engraved, drawn and painted copies after this, Michelangelo's celebrated original, which has belonged, among others, to Lawrence, William II of Holland and the Grand Duke of Saxe-Weimar. Datable to *c.*1533, it is one of the group of 'presentation drawings', of extremely refined technique, made for the artist's friends. Vasari named it 'Il Sogno' (1568) but did not explain the allegory. It may represent the Human Mind re-awakened by the trumpeting angel to the celestial sphere and Virtue, banishing the Vices (six of the seven deadly sins are shown, excluding Pride) and illusions (the masks beneath) of Man's earthly dreams. More usually, the flying figure is described as Fame. (Princes Gate Catalogue 139)

Jooes de Momper *(1564–1635)*

31 *Wooded Landscape with a Horse and Rider and Standard-bearer*

Traces of black chalk; pen and brown ink; brown wash, with drawing with the point of the brush; on white (now stained) laid paper. 22.7 × 18.1 cm.
Signed and dated in pen and brown ink, lower centre: 'Jooes de Momper/1598'
Verso: Franciscus Baedens (1571–1618), *Mercury and Venus, with Cupid*
Black and red chalk; dark brown and yellow-brown ink, with drawing with the point of the brush; touches of off-white and pink oil paint.
Signed in pen and brown ink, bottom left: 'franciscu ꞊ baedens/a roma 1596'.
Collectors' marks: Lord St. Helens; Woodburn (inscription on old mount).

WITT COLLECTION 3110

Since the early provenance of this sheet is unknown, it is a matter of speculation as to how two highly finished, signed and dated drawings by different artists should appear on the *recto* and *verso* of the same sheet. Matthias Winner's suggestion (*Pieter Bruegel der Älter als Zeichner*, Berlin, 1975, no. 202) that the sheet formed part of a collector's 'friendship album' is attractive, and may be borne out by the small format of the Momper drawing (other landscapes by this artist measure approx. 20 × 30 cm), by its prominent signature and date (rare in this artist's oeuvre), and by the decorative nature of the drawing, the subject matter of which is an amplification of a motif Momper often employed.

Girolamo Francesco Maria Mazzola, *called* Parmigianino *(1503–40)*

32 *The Healing of the Lame Man at the Beautiful Gate of the Temple(?)*

Pen and ink and wash heightened with white bodycolour. 20.8 × 15.6 cm.
Inscribed in pencil in various hands, on *verso*: 'Parmesan', and collectors' names. Collectors' marks: Lely; Lawrence; Barck; Calando (*recto* and *verso*).

PRINCES GATE COLLECTION 361

The subject (from *Acts*, 3, 1–10) proposed in the title is suggested by a resemblance to Raphael's tapestry design, after which Parmigianino made an etching and which evidently inspired him. The style confirms a date in the Roman period, 1524–7. The drawing was engraved in facsimile by F. Rosaspina, when in the collection of G.A. Armano.

Girolamo Francesco Maria Mazzola, *called* Parmigianino *(1503–40)*

33 *The Virgin(?) Spinning*

Black chalk heightened with white on light brown paper; traces of red chalk. 23.1 × 17.5 cm.
The *verso* is displayed here. Inscribed in ink over an older inscription, on both *recto* and *verso*, bottom right: 'Permegiano'; numerals on *recto*, 'No 29' (?) and *verso*, '92'.

Collector's mark: Ginsburg (*recto* and *verso*).
On the *recto*, in black chalk, heightened with white, a study of a seated woman, *S.Mary Magdalene*(?), formerly called '*S.Thais*'.

If the drawing indeed shows *The Virgin Spinning*, it would illustrate the story in the apocryphal *Book of James* (X–XII). Both sides of the sheet, however, have recently been thought to be studies from the life, contemporary with Parmigianino's work at Fontanellato, before he left for Rome in 1524. In the later 1520s the artist used the study on the *recto* for his etching, '*S.Thais*'. (Princes Gate Catalogue 173; *recto*)

Jacopo Carrucci da Pontormo
(1494–1556/7)

34 *Seated Youth*

Black chalk; the sheet splashed with (?) distemper.
40.4 × 28 cm.
Inscribed in red chalk on the *verso*, bottom right: 'Pont . . . (ormo?).
Collector's mark: Lawrence (Woodburn 1860 sale number 21(10), pencilled top right)
Verso: in red chalk, *Study for the Figure of S.Jerome in the 'Madonna Enthroned', Uffizi.*

This informal study of a youth in contemporary artisan dress, formerly in the Fenwick Collection, is apparently unconnected with any known painting. That on the *verso* is for a small altarpiece of which the execution and parts of the design are now attributed to Bronzino, *c.*1525, evidently with some assistance from his master. The same date for the *recto* is indicated by its style.

Johannes Stradanus *(1523–1605)*

35 *Pearl-diving*

Pencil; pen and brown ink, pale brown wash; heightening with white bodycolour; on very pale buff laid paper. The pictorial area enclosed within a ruled line in pen and brown ink. The sheet unevenly trimmed at all sides.
The white bodycolour used to efface figures, particularly at the centre of the sheet. 19.4 × 27.1 cm.
Inscribed by the artist in pen and brown ink, in the margin below the pictorial area: '. . . Balbi veneziano in Den Reÿse van indie de levanta(?) schet int isole de ormus Messehense de perlen op dese maniere maken op derde renden(?) pavaak . . .'

The inscription is almost impossible to decipher but is apparently an explanation of the circumstances under which the pearl-diving was sketched(?) by Balbi on an island in the Straits of Menina, while travelling from India. The drawing is difficult to date, but would seem to relate, in its exotic subject matter and dimensions, to a drawing of a unicorn hunt in India (untraced), engraved by J. Collaert after Stradanus, as one of the hunting scenes in the series *Venetiones Ferarum, Avium, Piscium* . . . (Hollstein, VII, 424–527: dimensions 19.4 × 26 cm). The present sheet, however, shows no signs of having been pressed through for engraving, but may have been a rejected design for the series.

Jacopo Tintoretto *(1518–94)*

36 *A Man, Seated*

Black chalk, heightened with white, on faded grey-green paper; surrounded by a black painted border. 27 × 19.4 cm.

No precisely corresponding figure has been found in Tintoretto's paintings, but a closely similar one is in *The Crucifixion* from S.Severo (Venice, Accademia), usually dated to 1554–5. Two further studies (Uffizi; Windsor), comparable in style, are evidently for figures in the same painting and confirm a date in the mid-1550s for the present sheet.

8

9

10

11

12

13

14

15

16

17

18

19

20

21

22

23

24

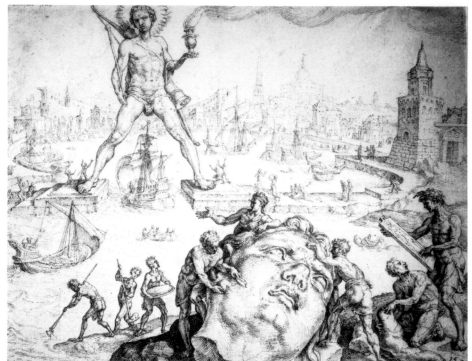

25

26

27

28

29 michel ange.

30

31

32

33

34

35

36

The Seventeenth Century

Annibale Carracci (1560–1609)

37 Wooded landscape with a Drinker

Traces of black chalk or pencil; pen and brown ink; on pale buff (now stained) laid paper. The sheet edged by a ruled line in pen and dark brown ink, laid down, and unevenly trimmed at all sides. 19.7 × 30.2 cm.
Numbered in an old hand, in pen and brown ink, top left: '509'. Inscribed and numbered in different modern hands in pencil, *verso*: 'A Carracci', and: '309'. Traces of an inscription in pencil, *verso*, masked by the overlap of the false margin.

WITT COLLECTION 3994

This lively and delicate drawing was confirmed by Rudolf Wittkower (*cf.* Sir Robert Witt's files, no. 3994) to be by the hand of Annibale.

Claude Gellée, *called* Claude Lorrain (1600–82)

38 Pastoral Scene in a Clearing in a Wood

Pen and brown wash over black chalk, slightly heightened with white bodycolour. 20.1 × 28.7 cm.
Collector's mark: Richardson Snr.
Verso: Study of a Tree, pen and ink with traces of black chalk.

PRINCES GATE COLLECTION 416

Evidently made in the studio, although in a technique reminiscent of Claude's studies from nature, this drawing appears to be an independent work, not related to a painting. It has been dated to the 1640s.

Claude Gellée, *called* Claude Lorrain (1600–82)

39 Study for 'The Arrival of Aeneas at Pallanteum'

Pencil, pen and brown ink and different shades of brown wash; corrections in white bodycolour. 18.3 × 25.2 cm.

Signed and dated, bottom left: 'Roma 1675 Claudio fecit.'
Inscribed by the artist across the hills to left and right with names of places mentioned in *Aeneid*: left, 'cittadella . . . Re Evandra . . . onte Evantine'; right (partly obscured by white bodycolour), '. . . ruine de la . . . ianicolo', '. . . saturno . . .' Squared with diagonals in pencil and surrounded by an ink frame-line.

PRINCES GATE COLLECTION 215

One of eight known studies for the painting of 1675 for Don Gasparo Altieri (Anglesey Abbey), this probably dates from *c*.1673, the date having been added later by the artist. The subject is from Virgil's *Aeneid*, VIII. The sheet comes from the 'Wildenstein Album', now Agnew's, formerly Odescalchi collection. (Princes Gate Catalogue 134)

Claude Gellée, *called* Claude Lorrain (1600–82)

40 Venus presenting Arms to Aeneas

Traces of pencil; pen and brown ink; grey-blue water-colour(?) wash, mixing in certain areas with the pencil; heightening with white and pale orange bodycolour (now largely oxidised) in the figures and chariot; on buff (now stained and unevenly discoloured) laid paper. The sheet laid down, and unevenly trimmed at all sides, apparently to a ruled line in pen and brown ink. 17.4 × 23.7 cm.
Signed in pen and brown ink, on a slip of paper trimmed from the bottom of the sheet: 'Claudio fecit/Roma 1670', and inscribed by the artist: 'Virgilio libro ottavo venera da L'arma a Enea'.
Collectors' marks: J. Richardson the Elder; Barnard (his mount); Lawrence; Esdaile (inscribed *recto* and *verso*).

GIFT OF LADY CHARLOTTE BONHAM-CARTER, 1965. WITT NO. 4740

This densely worked drawing, whose subject is taken from the *Aeneid*, Book VIII, is among Claude's first illustrations to Virgil (begun 1669), and is the only treatment of this subject in his oeuvre.

The drawing stands as an independent work, not executed in preparation for a painting. (*cf.* Marcel Roethlisberger, *Claude Lorrain The Drawings*, Berkeley and Los Angeles, 1969, no. 1026)

Sir Anthony van Dyck *(1599–1641)*

41 *Study of a Man bending forward and pulling, his right Arm outstretched; two Studies of the right Arm, a Study of the right Hand, and a Study of the left Hand*

Black chalk heightened with white chalk for all studies except that of the hand on the extreme right; charcoal for the hand on the extreme right only; on coarse pale buff (now stained) laid paper. The sheet unevenly trimmed at all sides, and laid down. 27 × 42.7 cm.
Inscribed in an old hand in pen and brown ink: 'Van Dyck'
Collector's marks: Lankrink; Richardson Snr (the drawing on his mount).

WITT COLLECTION 1664

The studies are for the figure of the soldier who drags at the fallen Christ's robe in the painting *The Carrying of the Cross*, executed in 1617 for St Pauluskerk, Antwerp.

Ian McNairn (*The Young Van Dyck*, National Gallery of Canada, Ottawa, 1980, no. 18) has noted that of the preparatory sketches for this painting, the present drawing is probably the only study from life, and it is likely, as J. Rupert Martin has observed, (*Van Dyck as a Religious Artist*, The Art Museum, Princeton University, 1979, no. 5), that it was executed after the *modello* (Stedelijk Prentenkabinet, Antwerp: Horst Vey, *Die Zeichnungen Anton van Dyck*, Brussels, 1963, no. 13).

The studies make clear van Dyck's intention to achieve the most dramatic statement of the soldier's arm and hand – other parts of the body are summarily sketched – and concentrate principally on the flow of contours rather than on the play of light over the musculature (already indicated in the Antwerp *modello*). The initial idea for the arm, at the centre of the sheet, is followed below by a stronger alternative position of the hand, closer to that in the *modello*. This new pose, modified, is rapidly explored in the study on the extreme left of the sheet, and finally reworked immediately to the right, with the hand repositioned to focus on the harsh profile of the knuckles, the position adopted in the final painting.

The study of the left hand, on the extreme right of the sheet, is probably a later addition, since the medium used here differs from that employed in the rest of the sheet.

Sir Anthony van Dyck *(1599–1641)*

42 *Moses and the Brazen Serpent*

Pen and brown ink; brown, and in restricted areas, grey wash with drawing with the brush; on pale buff (now stained) laid paper. The sheet unevenly trimmed on all sides, the top arched. 14.5 (maximum) × 20.5 cm.
Inscribed in pen and brown ink, *verso*: 'RPR' (Roupell), and in the same hand, on the old mount, with collectors' names.
Collectors' marks: Richardson Snr; Lawrence; Roupell (*cf.* inscription).
Verso: A Group of Israelites, a Study for the 'Mystic Marriage of St Catherine', and a Crab, in pen and brush and brown ink washes.

WITT COLLECTION 2365

The drawings on the *recto* (an initial fragmentary study at the bottom of the sheet is partly cut away) are early studies for the painting *Moses and the Brazen Serpent* (Prado, 1,673), and may be dated to 1621. It is the first sheet, out of seven known studies for the painting (Vey, *op. cit.*, nos. 43–9) in which is stated the full composition, which depends largely on Rubens' painting of the same subject. (Princes Gate Collection 15)

The group of Israelites on the *verso*, unidentified by Vey, is a tracing through and reworking of the figures supporting the falling woman, and is thus in reverse, anticipating the study in the Musée Bonnat (Vey no. 46) and the final painting, in which Moses stands on the right.

Previously ascribed to Adam Elsheimer *(1578–1610)*

43 *Landscape with a Wayfarer*

Brush drawing in brown and Indian ink, heightened with white bodycolour, on buff paper. Laid down. 19.6 × 32.1 cm.
Inscribed in ink in a later hand, bottom left: 'Rembrant', and in pencil on the mount, in an old hand: 'Elsheimar'.
Collectors' marks: West; Lawrence (Woodburn 1860 sale number, 380(1), pencilled on mount).

PRINCES GATE COLLECTION 254

This sheet, formerly in the Fenwick Collection, was previously celebrated as an outstanding example of Elsheimer's poetic 'landscape gouaches' (although itself not in gouache), all of which are now thought to date from the mid-seventeenth century at the earliest and to be by various artists. No new author for the present drawing has yet been seriously suggested.

Govaert Flinck (1615–60)

44 Seated Female Nude

Black chalk, heightened with white chalk; on blue (now discoloured and stained) laid paper. The sheet unevenly trimmed at all sides, apparently to a ruled line in black chalk. 31.7 × 22.7 cm.

WITT COLLECTION 4002

The drawing is one of thirty-seven studies of the female nude catalogued by J.W. von Moltke (Govaert Flinck 1615–1660, Amsterdam, 1965, no. D.202), the majority of which are in black and white chalk on blue paper. Other studies of the same model are in the collections of the late C.R. Rudolf (Moltke, no. D.199), the Prentenkabinet, Leyden (Moltke, nos. D.201, D.217, and D.221), and the Kupferstichkabinett, Berlin (Moltke, no. D.208). This last drawing is dated 1648, a date possibly shared by the other drawings of the same model. The Witt sheet, in common with Flinck's other academic figure studies (which he began in 1637), is greatly influenced by his friend and fellow-pupil in Rembrandt's studio, J.A. Backer.

Francesco Barbieri, called Guercino (1591–1666)

45 Aurora COLOUR PLATE III

Red chalk, with some rubbing or use of the stump, on off-white (now unevenly discoloured) laid paper. The sheet unevenly trimmed at all sides. 24.9 × 27.2 cm.

WITT COLLECTION 1328

One of eight sheets of preparatory drawings for the fresco ceiling-decoration Aurora, painted in 1621 for Pope Gregory xv and Cardinal Ludovico in the Casino Ludovisi, Rome. Denis Mahon (Il Guercino, Bologna, 1968, no. 78 and p. 89) has observed that of the preparatory drawings, four, and possibly five, sheets are studies for the figure of Aurora herself, in which the artist's experiments with iconography and formal inventiveness are displayed. The present sheet, which shows Aurora travelling in her chariot from right to left, is probably the first of the studies, since in the other drawings, and in the final painting, Aurora's direction is reversed, and the viewpoint lowered (indicated by the alternative position of the chariot wheel in the Witt drawing).

Francesco Barbieri, called Guercino (1591–1666)

46 Scene in a Kitchen

Pen and brown ink, and brush and brown wash; on pale cream (now unevenly discoloured and stained) laid paper. The sheet unevenly trimmed at all sides, apparently to a ruled line in pencil (visible top left). 26 × 40.3 cm. Numbered in a later hand in black chalk or graphite, bottom left: '3'

WITT COLLECTION 1347

This genre-scene, executed largely from life and influenced by Annibale Carracci, is, as Denis Mahon has noted (op. cit., no. 216, and pl. 201), an independent drawing made for its own sake, and unrelated to any painting. It displays, in common with many other sheets by this artist (see cat. nos. 45, 47) a richness of handling and a varying emphasis of forms.

Francesco Barbieri, called Guercino (1591–1666)

47 A Mother and Child

Red chalk (a dark red for the contours and drawing of the mother, an orange-red for the modelling of the child), with use of the stump or rubbing, and some drawing with the stump alone (in the back of the child); on coarse pale buff (now unevenly discoloured) laid paper. The sheet unevenly trimmed at all sides. 30.1 × 21 cm.

WITT COLLECTION 1327

The drawing, dated by Denis Mahon (*op. cit.* no. 187) to the last half of the 1620s, may have been a study for a painting whose exact subject matter, perhaps an *Allegory of Charity* or a *Holy Family*, cannot be precisely defined. The drawing was copied, also in red chalk, by Francesco Bartolozzi (Albertina, Vienna) who completed the head and shoulders of the seated woman.

Sir Peter Lely *(1618–80)*

48 *Two Heralds in Ceremonial Dress*

Detailed preliminary drawing in charcoal; black chalk (principally in the figure on the right), and heightening with white chalk applied with the brush; on blue (now unevenly discoloured and stained) laid paper. The drawing made up of four unevenly trimmed sheets, and unevenly trimmed at all sides, apparently to a ruled line in pen and brown ink. 51.8 × 36.4 cm.

WITT COLLECTION 1259

The drawing is one of thirty-one surviving sheets depicting figures from the Procession of the Order of the Garter, and one of the two extant drawings of Heralds. A third drawing of two Heralds, formerly in the Kupferstichkabinett, Berlin, was presumed lost during the Second World War. All except three of the drawings (*A Pursuivant* and *A Knight of the Garter* (Rijksmuseum, Amsterdam) and a *Knight of the Garter* (Private Collection, Holland)) are in black and white chalk on blue paper. Sir Oliver Millar (*Sir Peter Lely*, National Portrait Gallery, London, 1978, p. 81) has dated the series to the mid-1660s, although there is no contemporary reference to the drawings being executed for a specific commission, and no evidence that they were preparatory drawings for a larger work: indeed, as Millar (*ibid.*) has observed, the very confident and finished nature of the drawings makes this unlikely. It is certain, however, that in the production of these drawings Lely was influenced by van Dyck's oil sketch of the King and Knights of the Order in procession on St George's day, a picture almost certainly in the artist's possession by this time.

Adam Frans van der Meulen *(1632–90)*

49 *View of Courtrai*

Pencil; black ink, and restricted watercolour washes, with some drawing with the point of the brush; on off-white (now stained) laid paper. The drawing made up of three sheets, and unevenly trimmed at all sides. 38.3 × 128.8 cm. Inscribed in pen and brown ink, *verso:* 'Courtray Nᵒ 17 (the number deleted) Nᵒ 53'. Inscribed in the same hand in pencil, *verso:* 'Courtray'

WITT COLLECTION 4661

This panoramic watercolour, which can be dated to 1667, is related to a larger pen drawing (42 × 318 cm) in the collection of the Gobelins factory, Paris (*Inventaire Général des Richesses d'Art de la France, Paris, Monuments civils*, Tome III, 1902, p. 119, unnumbered), to a tapestry in Versailles (uncatalogued), and to a painting, *Vue de la marche de l'armée du Roi sur la Ville de Courtray qui fut prise le 18 juillet 1667*, also in Versailles (A. Pératé and G. Brière, *Musée National de Versailles, Compositions Historiques*, I, Paris, 1931, no. 263 (V.574)). A second painting of this subject, also in Versailles, mentioned in Soulie's catalogue of 1881 (Tome II, no. 2219; dimensions: 133 × 42 cm (?)) has not been traced. A third painting, *Louis XIV at Courtrai, 1667* (105.5 × 137.3 cm), whose background was also drawn from the present sheet, was with Tooth's, London, in 1958.

An engraving after the drawing was made in 1685 by F. Baudouins and J.B. Scotin (Hollstein, XIV, p. 18, no. 9).

Isack van Ostade *(1621–49)*

50 *Rear view of a House with Protective Roof and an attached Well*

Pen and brown ink, and brush and brown wash; black and red chalk; restricted watercolour washes, with drawing with the brush, and use of the dry brush; on pale cream (now unevenly discoloured) laid paper. The drawing made up of three irregularly trimmed sheets, edged by a ruled line in pen and brown ink, top and bottom, and unevenly trimmed at all sides, with angled corners. The figures of a man and woman, in black chalk with touches of red, abandoned at the right of the drawing. 17.9 × 20.3 cm.

Inscribed in pen and brown ink, bottom centre: 'Jh', and in a different hand in pencil, *verso*: 'Av. ostade', and numbered in various contemporary hands.
Collectors' marks: Hugford (inscription, *recto*); H.Füssli & Cie (*verso*).

WITT COLLECTION 3991

This study, purchased by Sir Robert Witt as by Adriaen van Ostade, and subsequently exhibited as by him, has been convincingly reattributed to his brother Isack by Bernhard Schnackenburg (*Adriaen van Ostade Isack van Ostade Zeichnungen und Aquarelle*, Hamburg, 1981, no. 571). The drawing may be dated to the last three years of the artist's short life (1646–49), during which he studied various types of peasant houses and villages. A drawing of a *Two-storied House with Pigeon-loft* (Boymans-van Beuningen Museum, Rotterdam: Schnackenberg no. 569) can be related to the present sheet in the handling of the foliage, the inclusion of figures at the right of the drawing, and in the range of media employed.

Isack van Ostade *(1621–49)*

51 *A reeling Drunkard, brandishing a Tankard*

Pen and brown ink; brown ink washes of varying strengths, with drawing with the brush; on cream paper. The pictorial area enclosed within a ruled line in pen and brown ink. The sheet unevenly trimmed on all sides. Vestiges of white bodycolour, and creases, at the bottom of the sheet.
15.5 × 8.2 cm.
Inscribed in pen and pale brown ink, lower right: 'o va' (the 'va' in monogram), and below, in pen and dark brown ink: 'av.o' (the 'av' in monogram).

WITT COLLECTION 3755

This drawing, unknown to Schnackenburg (*op. cit.*) was formerly attributed to Adriaen van Ostade. However, the deeper characterisation of the figure, the stronger chiaroscuro, and the more particularised treatment of the play of light over the forms suggest that the drawing may be given to Isack. Schnackenburg attributes to Isack some eight studies of standing or seated men, all datable to 1641–42, of which his no. 435, a *Study of a seated man*, (Amsterdam Historisch Museum,

no. 18 0 87, also previously attributed to Adriaen) is analogous to the present sheet.

Isaac Oliver *(1556?–1617)*

52 *Five Sheets of Figure Studies, on one Mount*

A resting Woman (top left)
Pen and pale brown ink; brown and grey ink washes, with drawing with the point of the brush; on white (now unevenly discoloured) laid paper. The sheet unevenly trimmed at all sides. 8.9 × 8.2 cm.
Verso: Study of a man, in pen and pale brown ink.

Twelve Male and Female Heads; a reclining draped Female (top right)
Pen and grey ink; on white (now stained) laid paper. The sheet trimmed to an irregular octagon. *Maxima:* 4.7 × 5.8 cm.

Rear view of a seated Woman, turning to the left (centre, right)
Pen and grey-brown and grey ink; grey-brown and grey ink washes, with drawing with the point of the brush; on white (now stained) laid paper. The sheet unevenly trimmed at all sides. 6 × 6.3 cm.

A Woman playing a Lute (bottom left)
Pen and pale brown ink; brown and grey ink washes, with drawing with the point of the brush; on white (now unevenly discoloured) laid paper. The sheet unevenly trimmed at all sides. 9.4 × 8.3 cm.

A standing Youth, and two Male Heads (bottom right)
Pen and pale brown ink; on white laid paper. The sheet unevenly trimmed at the top, left and right, the bottom uneven. 7.4 × 6.5 cm.

WITT COLLECTION 2390 a–e

The five drawings on this mount date variously from *c.*1600–*c.*1610 (*cf.* Jill Finsten, *Isaac Oliver, Art at the Courts of Elizabeth I and James I*, New York and London, 1981, nos. 201–5 inclusive).

The studies of single figures relate to the allegorical and mythological female figures in the British Museum (Finsten nos. 191, 192, 197 and 198). The handling of the five studies falls into three distinct categories: the first, employing a dense hatching with a hooked stroke, top centre and bottom right; the second, hatching with a straighter stroke, with the inclusion of stippling, as in the drawings centre, right, and bottom left; lastly, drawing with a finer line and regular, diagonal hatching, combined with curly contours (top right). Finsten connects the first two types of handling with that employed by H. Goltzius and J. de Gheyn, itself influenced by engraving, while the studies of heads are indebted to the style adopted by the two Dutch artists when interpreting the drawings of Leonardo da Vinci, during the last decade of the sixteenth century and the first decade of the seventeenth.

Rembrandt van Rijn *(1606–69)*

53 *The Liberation of S. Peter*

Pen and ink with *pentimenti* in a different ink; traces of white bodycolour. 16.4 × 25.3 cm.
Collector's mark: Friedrich August II of Saxony.

PRINCES GATE COLLECTION 196

The expressive introspection of this drawing, apparently of *c*.1650–55, may be contrasted with the more dramatic interpretation in an earlier drawing of the same subject (Frankfurt, Städelsches Kunstinstitut), dated to *c*.1648–9. The pentimenti have been attributed to a later hand, but are probably by the artist. A very close copy is at Brunswick (Herzog Anton Ulrich Museum).

Rembrandt van Rijn *(1606–69)*

54 *A Quack addressing a Crowd at a Fair*
COLOUR PLATE IV

Pen and ink and wash, heightened with traces of white bodycolour; attempts at erasure, probably by a later hand, of the child in the foreground. 18.8 × 16.6 cm.
Collector's mark: Friedrich August II of Saxony.

PRINCES GATE COLLECTION 186

A drawing of a similar scene (Berlin, Kupferstichkabinett) is sometimes thought to show the same incident from a different viewpoint; it appears however to be slightly earlier than the present sheet, which was dated on grounds of style at one time to *c*.1637 or earlier, and more recently to *c*.1638–42.

Rembrandt van Rijn *(1606–69)*

55 *Two Studies of Saskia*

Red chalk. 15.5 × 13.7 cm.

PRINCES GATE COLLECTION 184

Rembrandt married Saskia van Ulenborch in 1634; she died eight years later after giving birth to four children, of whom only Titus lived more than a few months. These studies appear to show Saskia as an invalid, seen by artificial light. They are comparable with a number of other drawings of the artist's wife in sickness or confinement, including two more in the Princes Gate collection (inv. nos. 183, 185) also in red chalk, all apparently of the later 1630s.

Sir Peter Paul Rubens *(1577–1640)*

56 *God the Father supported by Cherubim (after Pordenone)*

Black and red chalk and watercolour, touches of bodycolour. Backed. 34.7 × 45.3 cm.
Inscribed in ink, bottom right: '109'.
Collectors' marks: Mariette; von Fries; Lawrence.

PRINCES GATE COLLECTION 50

One of many copies after other masters by Rubens, this shows Pordenone's cupola fresco (1520) in the Malchiostro Chapel, S. Niccolò, Treviso (destroyed 1944). It is the first evidence of Rubens' interest in ceiling painting, dating from his earliest years in Italy, 1600 or soon after. The flight of *putti* reappears years later in several compositions of *The Assumption of the Virgin*. The sheet, which once belonged to Crozat, comes from the Fenwick Collection.

Sir Peter Paul Rubens *(1577–1640)*

57 *Helena Fourment* FRONT COVER

Black, red (and white?) chalk, heightened with white bodycolour; pen and ink details of the head; touching up by a later hand of the head-dress, in black chalk and brush and ink. The figure cut round in silhouette, restored in outline, inlaid and backed. 61.2 × 55 cm.

PRINCES GATE COLLECTION 64

The portrait probably dates from the time of Rubens' marriage in 1630 to Helena Fourment (1614–73). She appears to be dressed for church and is holding a prayerbook with a gloved hand. With her bare right hand she draws back the *huke*, a fashionable all-enveloping garment which was suspended from a tasselled skullcap and reached the ground, protecting the wearer from the elements. The sheet is exceptional among Rubens' drawings in its scale and its rich and elaborate technique. It is presumably not a preparatory study for a painting, but an independent portrait. (Princes Gate Catalogue 147)

Sir Peter Paul Rubens *(1577–1640)*

58 *Study for the 'Bath of Diana'*

Pen and ink. 29 × 50.9 cm.
Inscribed indistinctly in red chalk by the artist, on *verso*, top centre: 'dese dry vraukens(?) half ghecleurt(?) door van den Broeck'.
Collectors' marks: Lankrink; Richardson Jnr.
Verso: Study for the Munich 'Lion Hunt', red and black chalk.

PRINCES GATE COLLECTION 65

The drawing on the *verso* is for a painting of *c.*1622; for that on the *recto*, dates in the later 1620s, the early 1630s or, more convincingly, the later 1630s have been proposed. The studies are for Rubens' so-called *Bath of Diana* (Rotterdam, Museum Boymans-van Beuningen), the surviving right half of a damaged *Diana and Actaeon*, clearly inspired by Titian's painting of the subject (Sutherland Collection, National Gallery of Scotland), which Rubens would have seen in Spain. (Princes Gate Catalogue 148)

Moses Ter Borch *(1645–67)*

59 *A Standing Youth holding a Staff*

Black chalk; on coarse buff laid paper. The sheet unevenly

trimmed at all sides. 23.8 × 8.3 cm.
Numbered in an old hand in pencil, *verso:* '6i'

WITT COLLECTION 2204

One of a series of numbered studies, probably from an album (*cf.* C. von Hasselt, *Dutch Drawings from the Seventeenth Century*, New York and Paris, 1977–8, no. 15), which concentrate on the play of light upon a single male figure. The studies, all of which are in either red or black chalk on warm-toned paper, may be assigned to a date at the end of the artist's short life, on the basis of a comparable drawing, dated January 1660, in the Baltimore Museum of Art.

The models, who are all sailors, cabin boys etc, appear to have been posed under controlled light conditions, and in some cases were studied more than once (the present model is the subject of a red chalk drawing in the Lugt Coll., Paris, no. 5111).

Willem van der Velde the Younger *(1633–1707)*

60 *Scene in an Estuary, with Two Fishing Pinks and a Saluting Frigate*

Pencil; on white (now unevenly discoloured) laid paper. The sheet unevenly trimmed at all sides. Backed with tissue. 37.1 × 50.6 cm.

WITT COLLECTION 1256

This large-scale and confident drawing is similar in its vigorous and broad handling to the drawing of *Two English Frigates before the Wind* (*cf.* M.S. Robinson *The Van der Velde Drawings in the National Maritime Museum*, Vol. II, London, 1974, no. 1113) and may be of a similar date, i.e. *c.*1675.

37

38

39

40

41

42

43

44

45

46

47

48

49

50

51

52

53

54

55

56

57

58

60

59

The Eighteenth Century

François Boucher (1703–70)

61 A Wooded Landscape with a River, Bridge and Houses

Black and white chalk, with extensive use of rubbing or the stump; on blue-grey (now unevenly discoloured and stained) laid paper. The sheet made up at the bottom left and right, and top right corners, and unevenly trimmed at all sides, apparently to a ruled line in pencil. 40.2 × 52.9 cm.

WITT COLLECTION 3439

The drawing appears to be an independent work, unrelated to a painting, and too unspecific, and too large, to be a preliminary study for an engraving. It has a delicacy and softness of manner also visible in the sheet *Thatched Mill Cottages with Two Trees at the Edge of a Stream* (coll. Pierpont Morgan Library, exhibited *François Boucher in North American Collections: 100 Drawings*, National Gallery of Art, Washington, D.C., 1973, no. 59).

François Boucher (1703–70)

62 A Study of a Peasant Woman with Two Children, Two Studies of Cows, and a Study of Cows and Sheep (four drawings and five etchings on one mount)

All drawings in dark brown chalk; on off-white (now stained) laid paper.

A Peasant Woman with Two Children (centre range, right) The sheet unevenly trimmed at all sides. 18.5 × 10.2 cm.

A Cow, facing right (bottom range, left) The sheet unevenly trimmed to an irregular five-sided figure. *Maxima*: 6.6 × 9.3 cm.

Three Cows and Sheep (bottom range, centre) The sheet unevenly trimmed to an irregular eight-sided figure. *Maxima*: 8 × 18.6 cm.

A Cow, facing left (bottom range, right) The sheet unevenly trimmed. *Maxima*: 8.1 × 10.7 cm.

Five soft-ground etchings on off-white (now stained) laid paper. All sheets unevenly trimmed at all sides, and of varying dimensions. The etchings, top range, centre, corrected by Hubert Robert in pen and brown ink. The drawings and prints laid down on Hubert Robert's mount. Inscribed in pencil and superimposed in pen and black ink, on the mount, bottom right: 'Collection Hubert Robert', and in the same hand, in pencil, on the back of the mount: 'Ces dessins proviennent de la collection Hubert Robert, vendue en 1809'. Numbered in blue crayon on the mount, bottom left: '25', and in graphite ('pencil') bottom right: '+ D 25392', and in various hands in graphite ('pencil') on the back of the mount: '6', '3', and: '159'. Collector's mark: Delatigny.

WITT COLLECTION 4706

The drawings are probably all late works. The studies of cows are reminiscent of those included in the late paintings, such as *The Exodus of the Shepherds*, Nelson Gallery, Atkins Museum, USA.

The etchings are by various hands, including those of Demarteau (top, centre), and O'Rior (top right).

Giovanni Antonio Canal, called Canaletto (1697–1768)

63 A Standing Man, viewed from the front

Pencil; pen and brown ink; on off-white (now stained) laid paper. The sheet unevenly trimmed at all sides. 30 × 17.4 cm. Inscribed by the artist in pen and brown ink, top right, *recto*: '11/uolta', the inscription repeated, *verso*. *Verso: A Standing Man in a Cloak, viewed from the rear*, in pencil, and pen and brown ink.

WITT COLLECTION 346

The figures on the *recto* and *verso* of the sheet are incorporated, side by side, in the right foreground of the painting *S. Giacomo di Rialto* (National Gallery of Canada, Ottawa: Constable and Links, *Canaletto*, Oxford, 1976, no. 298), which may be dated to *c*.1746 (Constable and Links, *op. cit.*, no. 298). Ruth Bromberg (*Canaletto . . .*, Fondazione Giorgio Cini, Venice, 1982, no. 120) has noted the similarity between the cloaked figure on the *verso* of the Witt sheet, and that in the background, left, of the etching *Mestre* (Ruth Bromberg, *Canaletto's Etchings*, London and New York, 1974, no. 3).

A similar sheet, with a large-scale figure study on the *recto* and *verso* and similarly inscribed, is in the Metropolitan Museum, New York (Constable and Links, *op. cit.*, no. 840).

Giovanni Antonio Canal,
called Canaletto (*1697–1768*)

64 *The Piazza di S.Giacomo di Rialto*

Pencil, pen and brown ink and grey washes. 31.8 (30.4 drawing; 1.4 joined strip) × 43.3 cm.
Signed in ink on strip of joined paper along lower edge, bottom left: 'Antonio Canal del', and inscribed by the artist: 'Piazza di S.Giaccomo di Rialto in Venezia, con parte del Famoso Ponte in distanza, Versso S.Bartolm:ᶜᵒ'
Collectors' marks: Lagoy; Dimsdale (*verso*).

PRINCES GATE COLLECTION 132

The style and rich technique of this sheet indicate a late date in the 1760s. Changes in the appearance of the buildings represented suggest that the artist used earlier sketches as well as up-to-date ones to compose this drawing. Four other versions of this view, of different dates, include a painting for which cat. no. 63 in this exhibition is a study. (Princes Gate Catalogue 130)

Giovanni Antonio Canal,
called Canaletto (*1697 1768*)

65 *A View from Somerset Gardens looking towards London Bridge*

Pen and brown ink and grey washes. On left side restored with inset square of paper, (*c.*7 × 7 cm). 23.4 × 72.6 cm.

PRINCES GATE COLLECTION 131

The panorama, from the terrace of Old Somerset House to London Bridge, was probably constructed, not with a *camera obscura*, but from copious studies made from various sites. This is perhaps Canaletto's earliest version of the view; others include another drawing and a painting in the Royal Collection. Canaletto spent ten years in England from 1746. (Princes Gate Catalogue 129)

Giovanni Antonio Canal,
called Canaletto (*1697–1768*)

66 *View of the Palazzo dei Mocenigo and other Buildings, from the Grand Canal*

Pen and brown ink; on white (now unevenly discoloured and stained) laid paper. The sheet unevenly trimmed at all sides, and backed with Japanese tissue. 19.6 × 28.1 cm.
Inscribed by the artist in pencil or black chalk, top: 'Altra veduta nella . . .' (the rest of the inscription largely effaced and illegible).
Collector's mark: Chariatte (inscription, *verso*)

WITT COLLECTION 4646

This rapid sketch, taken from ground level, includes (from left to right), four palaces belonging to the Mocenigo family, the Cantarini dalle Figure and the Palazzo Erizzo. It is a preliminary study for the right section of the painting *The Grand Canal: looking North-East from the Palazzo Balbi to the Rialto Bridge* (Collection Duke of Bedford, Woburn Abbey: W.G. Constable, *Canaletto*, revised by J.G. Links, Oxford, 1976, no. 215) and its second version in Bergamo (Constable and Links, *op. cit.*, no. 212), and may therefore be dated to *c.*1730 (Constable and Links, *op. cit.*, no. 589). The sketch was later re-used in part of the background of the oil *A Regatta on the Canal* (Collection H.M. The Queen, Windsor: Constable and Links, *op. cit.*, no. 347).

Jean Honoré Fragonard (*1732–1806*)

67 *'La Résignée'; the Artist's Daughter, Rosalie(?)*

Red chalk. Laid down. 22.5 × 17.2 cm.
Signed and dated, bottom left: 'frago. 1785'. Inscribed on

the mount: 'H.Fragonard 1765'.
Collector's mark: Goncourt; unidentified mark on mount.

PRINCES GATE COLLECTION 229

The date, which has been misread as 1765, is certainly 1785, as the style of the drawing confirms. The sitter appears to be the artist's daughter, Rosalie, who died of consumption in 1788 at the age of 18. She may be the subject of a number of other red chalk drawings of this period. (Princes Gate Catalogue 135)

Francesco Guardi *(1712–93)*

68 *The Feast of Ascension Day*

Pen and ink and wash over black chalk. 19.6 × 38.8 cm.
Collector's mark: Paulme.

PRINCES GATE COLLECTION 138

At the annual feast day in Venice recorded here the Doge rode out to the Lido in the State Barge, the 'Bucintoro' (seen here near the centre), to perform the marriage ritual between Venice and the sea. The church of S.Maria della Salute is indicated faintly on the right in chalk. The drawing, one of a number of views of the ceremony by Guardi, has been dated either to the early 1780s, or as among his last works. (Princes Gate Catalogue 136)

Jean-Baptiste Oudry *(1686–1755)*

69 *The Gardens at Arcueil(?)*

Traces of pencil; black and white chalk, with use of the stump or rubbing; on buff (now unevenly discoloured and stained) laid paper. The sheet edged by a later hand(?) with a ruled line in pen and brown ink. The figures of a strolling man and woman emerging from the allée, left, partly erased, partly effaced with white chalk and pale orange bodycolour. Two other pairs of figures, left of centre, similarly effaced. A fourth couple(?) under the second arch of the trellis, right, effaced with black chalk. 30.5 × 52.3 cm.
Signed in pen and dark brown ink, lower right: 'JB oudry 1745' (the 'JB' in monogram). Inscribed in an old hand in

black chalk, *verso*: 'Promenade dans un Parc par J B:Oudry Peintre du Roy Louis xv/Ecole francaise', and numbered and priced in different hands.

WITT COLLECTION 4656

The drawing, traditionally thought to be of the grounds of the Prince de Guise's château at Arcueil (destroyed 1752), is one of over a hundred sheets of garden subjects by Oudry, of which only a few are inscribed as having been executed at Arcueil (*cf.* Hal N. Opperman, *Jean Baptiste Oudry*, Vol. II, New York and London, 1977, D 1061 and p. 849). Oudry is also known to have worked at Voré and the Château d'Ivry, the home of the Marquis of Beringhen.

The strolling couples (now largely effaced) may have been by a hand other than Oudry's.

Giovanni Battista Piranesi *(1720–88)*

70 *Imaginary view of Quays in a City*

Red chalk; pen and brown ink and brown wash, with drawing with the point of the brush; touches of pencil; on white laid paper. The sheet unevenly torn, top, and unevenly trimmed at all other sides. 15.6 × 21.7 cm.
Signed in pen and brown ink, bottom left: 'Piranesi'.

WITT COLLECTION 4004

The drawing, dated by Hylton Thomas to 1745–50 (*The Drawings of Giovanni Battista Piranesi*, London, 1954, no. 22) belongs to a group of some fifteen sheets, eight of which (Thomas, *op. cit.*, nos. 4, 6, 7, 10, 27B, 34 and 44) are in the Kunsthalle, Hamburg. The group of drawings was executed during a brief period of five years, and all were signed and mounted by the artist (the mount has been removed from the present sheet), an indication of the value which he placed on them at this time.

Thomas (*op. cit.*, p. 17) has observed that this may be one of the first drawings in which Piranesi began consciously to exploit the effects of colour achieved by overlaying red and black chalk and an ink which has a slight golden hue, reminiscent of that used by Tiepolo.

Out of the group of drawings, that which most closely compares with the Witt sheet in linear exuberance and luminosity is the *Fantastic Monument* (Boston Museum of Fine Arts: Thomas, no. 25).

Hubert Robert *(1733–1808)*

71 *The Tivoli Gardens*

Red chalk. 32.5 × 44 cm.

PRINCES GATE COLLECTION 232

Fragonard and Hubert Robert spent the summer of 1760 at the Villa d'Este, Tivoli, with the Abbé de Saint-Non. Each made numerous red chalk drawings in this format of the gardens; this example illustrates their proximity of style at that time. It has usually been ascribed to Fragonard, but the more schematic and less subtle technique indicates the work of Robert.

Giovanni Battista Tiepolo *(1696–1770)*

72 *The Holy Family with S. Joseph Reading*
COLOUR PLATE VI

Pen and ink and wash. Laid down. 28.4 × 21.5 cm.
Collector's mark: Rudolf (on mount)

PRINCES GATE COLLECTION 159

There are a large number of pen drawings by Tiepolo of the Holy Family, similar in type to the present one and generally dated to the 1750s; two more are in this collection (inv. nos. 158, 386). The present sheet, which is in a very fresh condition, has been dated to *c.*1757. (Princes Gate Catalogue 151)

Giovanni Battista Tiepolo *(1696–1770)*

73 *Portrait of one of the Artist's Sons(?)*

Red chalk, heightened with white, on blue paper. Trimmed unevenly. *c.*23.5 × 16.1 cm.
Inscribed on *verso*: 'Xrs 12. No. 3465' (price and serial number possibly in Domenico Tiepolo's hand).

PRINCES GATE COLLECTION 161

The identification of the sitter is traditional; Lorenzo is apparently the most likely candidate, and *c.*1751–3, the years in Würzburg, the most probable date. The sheet comes from the 'Wendland Sketchbook'; a copy, perhaps by Lorenzo, is in the 'Würzburg Third Sketchbook'. (Princes Gate Catalogue 150)

Giovanni Battista Tiepolo *(1696–1770)*

74 *Satyr and Satyress*

Pen and ink and wash over black chalk. Backed. 14.7 × 27 cm. Inscribed in pencil in a later hand: 'Tiepolo', and in ink on the *verso* of the backing sheet: 'Giovanni Battista Tiepolo B. Venice 1697. D. Madrid 1770'.

PRINCES GATE COLLECTION 380

Previously associated with the satyrs in Tiepolo's ceiling painting at the Palazzo Clerici, Milan, and dated to *c.*1740, this drawing appears, however, to be later than others with satyrs for that ceiling. It seems that Domenico Tiepolo knew this design in 1757 when he painted his satyrs in the Foresteria of the Villa Valmarana, and the recently proposed connection with the decoration of the ballroom of the Villa Pisani at Strà, 1760–62, would probably place the drawing too late. (Princes Gate Catalogue 149)

Giovanni Domenico Tiepolo *(1727–1804)*

75 *A Ball at the Ridotto*

Pen and ink. 12.9 × 26.8 cm.
Signed in lighter ink, lower right: 'domenico Tiepolo invento e fece', and in ink, on the *verso*: the 'Stuttgart' inventory number, 'No. 2878; i.f.C.M(?)', all probably in the artist's hand; later pencilled numerals.
Verso: The rear part of a Coach, red chalk.

PRINCES GATE COLLECTION 163

Formerly called *A Ballroom Scene*, this drawing has been dated to the period of Domenico's work at the Villa Valmarana (1757). It is related to the painting, *The Dance in the Country* (Wrightsman Collection; variant, Louvre), where the dancing couple reappear with few variations and the rear of a coach repeats the design on the present *verso*.

Antoine Watteau *(1684–1721)*

76 *A Faun* COLOUR PLATE V

Black, red and white chalk on buff paper. 28.5 × 21.1 cm.
Collectors' marks: Baron Schwiter; unidentified.

PRINCES GATE COLLECTION 221

This drawing 'aux trois crayons' is one of three known studies for *L'Automne*, from the series, *The Seasons*, painted by Watteau for Crozat's dining room. The painting is lost, but was engraved by Faissar. The date of '*Les Saisons Crozats*' is not known, but the evident influence of Venetian art might suggest a date soon after rather than before 1715, the year Crozat returned from Italy with a collection of Italian and especially Venetian works of art. (Princes Gate Catalogue 153)

Antoine Watteau *(1684–1721)*

77 *A Friar standing ('Un Carme')*

Red and black chalk. 33.3 × 23.2 cm.
Collector's mark on former mount: Heseltine.

PRINCES GATE COLLECTION 220

The figure was etched in reverse by Boucher in the *Figures de différents Caractères . . .,* 1726–8 (34), of Julienne, to whom this sheet belonged. It can be associated with Watteau's series of 'character' drawings, portraits of Savoyards and other popular types, and is datable perhaps to *c.*1712–14. Although the sheet may be intended as a finished work of art, the slight background sketch of a church may indicate a projected painting like *La Marmotte* (Leningrad, Hermitage).

Antoine Watteau *(1684–1721)*

78 *A Sheet of Studies after Old Masters*

Red chalk. 17.7 × 29.1 cm.

PRINCES GATE COLLECTION 224

The Holy Family sketched on the right reappears in the picture, *The Marriage of S.Catherine*, shown within *L'Enseigne de Gersaint* (Berlin, Schloss Charlottenburg) of 1720. This late date for the drawing may be confirmed by the freedom and virtuosity of its technique. The Marriage of S.Catherine on the left of the sheet bears a certain resemblance to Veronese's painting then in Crozat's collection (Leningrad, Hermitage).

Giuseppe Valeriani *(died 1761)*

79 *Design for a Stage-set in Six Flats, the fore-ground Flat in Two Parts*

Pencil or black chalk; pen and brown and black ink, and restricted watercolour washes, with drawing with the pen and point of the brush; gold paint; on off-white (now stained) laid paper. Each flat roughly cut out and laid down; the second flat from the rear with cut out and pasted additions. *Minima*: 19.3 × 29.3 cm; *maxima*: 46 × 51.1 cm.

WITT COLLECTION 3925

This well-preserved design probably dates from Valeriani's Russian period (from 1742 until his death), when he was employed as stage-designer to the Court at St Petersburg.

A slighter cut-out design, also from the collection of Sir Robert Witt, and comparable in style and architectural features to the present work, but incorporating an equestrian portrait of the Russian Empress Elizabeth II, passed through Sotheby's, 13 December 1973, Lot no. 71.

Alexander Cozens (1700/1705–86)

80 A Mountain Lake or River among Rocks

Brush and black ink wash; on pale buff laid paper, prepared with a ground of pale brown ink (?) wash. The sheet unevenly trimmed at all sides, and laid down on the artist's mount. 23.3 × 31.3 cm.
Signed in pen and pale grey ink on the mount, left: 'Alex.ʳ Cozens', and numbered by the artist in pencil, top right: '54', the '4' over a 'o'.

WITT COLLECTION 1152

Although this drawing is not a 'blot' image of the most abstract type (such as those demonstrated in the artist's *A New Method of Assisting the Invention in Original Compositions of Landscape*, published in 1785), it is schematic, and shares many compositional features of 'Blot 13' – 'a hollow'. The drawing is on fairly thin paper, and while there is a possibility that it is a worked-up tracing from a 'blot', it seems more likely to have been directly 'blotted' on to the sheet. The alteration of the numbering at the top of the sheet is indicative of Cozens' continual activity of arranging, mounting, and classifying his drawings.

Alexander Cozens (1700/1705–86)

81 A Blasted Tree in a Landscape

Touches of pencil; pen and the point of the brush in brown ink washes; slight additions of gum or varnish in the foreground darks; on very thin laid paper, prepared with a ground of dilute varnish. The drawing edged with vestiges of a ruled line in pen and black ink, and laid down on the artist's mount. 31.5 × 40.5 cm.
Signed in pen and grey ink on the mount, left: 'Alex.ʳ Cozens.', and inscribed in pencil, top right of drawing: 'B'. Numbered in a modern hand on the back of the mount: 'A21365'.

SPOONER COLLECTION 29

This highly detailed drawing, of a scale near to the largest on which Cozens worked (which is approximately 45 × 62 cm), is in the artist's more graphic manner, and is related in style to

such drawings as *A Rocky Wooded Landscape with an Eagle and Its Prey*, ex-collection Randall-Davies, sold Sotheby's, 27 June 1968, Lot no. 70. The drawing's imagery is a combination of that of the *Classical Landscape* (Oppé Collection, exhibited *Alexander Cozens*, Sheffield and London, 1946, no. 56) with that of the small drawing of *Dead Trees* (collection Sir H. Theobald, exhibited *Alexander Cozens*, Sheffield and London, 1946, no. 58).

The paper has been made transparent probably by the addition of a ground of turpentine or mastic varnish mixed with spirit of turpentine, the recipe set out in Rule II of *A New Method . . .* (see cat. no. 80), and it is almost certain that the present image was initially traced through from a 'blot'.

John Robert Cozens (1752–97)

82 London from Greenwich Hill

Pencil; black and brown ink, and restricted watercolour washes, with some drawing with the point of the brush, and the use of the dry brush; re-drawing of foreground detail with pen and point of the brush in blue-grey wash, and black and brown ink; on off-white (now unevenly discoloured) wove paper. The sheet unevenly trimmed at all sides, apparently to a ruled line in pencil. 36.9 × 53.5 cm.
Signed in pen and black ink, bottom left of centre: 'Jn.º Cozens'.

SPOONER COLLECTION 30

C.F. Bell and T. Girtin, *J.R. Cozens*, 'Walpole Society' Annual Volume no. 23, 1934–5, no. 441, i and ii, and *Notes*, no. 441, record three versions of this subject, to which can be added a drawing in the collection of H.G. Balfour (Francis Hawcroft, *op. cit.*, no. 94), a drawing in the Yale Center for British Art, New Haven (*cf.* Andrew Wilton, *The Art of Alexander and John Robert Cozens*, Yale Center, 1980, no. 137), and the present sheet. All versions of the drawing, which differ principally in the number and arrangement of deer in the foreground, may be dated either to 1791 (on the basis of the date on Bell and Girtin, *op. cit.*, no. 441 i) or at the latest to 1792/3, after which date Cozens was unable to work.

John Robert Cozens *(1752–97)*

83 *The Castel Sant' Angelo, Rome*

Pencil; black ink, and blue watercolour washes; some slight scraping out; on white (now unevenly discoloured) laid paper. The sheet unevenly trimmed on all sides, and laid down on the artist's mount. 36 × 52.6 cm.
Signed in pen and black ink, bottom left of centre: 'Jn.° Cozens 1780'. Inscribed in a later hand in pencil, on the back of the mount: 'Castel of St Angelo *Rome*/J.R. Cozens 1780'.

SPOONER COLLECTION 31

The drawing, dated 1780, was executed in England after the artist's first journey to Switzerland and Italy (1776–9) in the company of Richard Payne Knight. It is the only published drawing of this subject (recorded by C.F. Bell and T. Girtin, *op. cit.*, no. 117), although vestiges of ruled pencil lines spaced at regular intervals underlying the area of the castle would indicate a partial squaring up, and almost certainly from a detailed preliminary drawing.

The subject of the Castel Sant'Angelo, presented less majestically, and viewed from a different angle, was treated by J.R. Cozens in one of his rare etchings, published posthumously by J.F. Thompson in *Original Studies from Nature by Various Artists*, 1801.

John Robert Cozens *(1752–97)*

84 *In the Canton of Unterwalden*

Pencil; black and brown ink, and watercolour wash, with drawing with the point of the brush; touches of dilute white and other coloured bodycolour; slight scraping and rubbing in the smoke and figures, left; on off-white (now slightly discoloured) laid paper. The sheet unevenly trimmed on all sides, apparently to a ruled line in pencil. 34 × 50.8 cm.
Numbered by the artist(?) in brush and grey wash, *verso*: '3', and in pencil: '3g' or: '39', and inscribed: 'To be copied'.

SPOONER COLLECTION 32

The drawing is one of four (the third(?) *cf.* inscriptions) versions of the subject, executed after Cozens' first Italian tour (see cat. no. 83). The other drawings are in the Lupton Bequest, Leeds City Art Gallery, the National Gallery of Ireland, Dublin (*cf.* Bell and Girtin, *op. cit.*, nos. 29 i and ii, respectively), and in the Cecil Higgins Art Gallery, Bedford (*cf.* Francis Hawcroft, *Watercolours by John Robert Cozens*, Whitworth Art Gallery, Manchester, and Victoria & Albert Museum, London, 1971, no. 9).

The Leeds drawing, although smaller than the present sheet (23.5 × 36.2 cm), is almost identical in its composition, particularly in the number and clarity of arrangement of foreground trees. The Dublin drawing, which includes so great a number of foreground trees that the eye is prevented from sweeping over the landscape, may pre-date the other versions.

Edward Dayes *(1763–1804)*

85 *View of Ullswater, Lake District*

Pencil; brown ink, and restricted watercolour wash, with some drawing with the brush; on off-white (now stained) laid paper. The drawing enclosed by a feigned mount in buff and buff-grey washes, with ruled lines in pen and grey-brown ink. The sheet unevenly trimmed at all sides, the corners angled. Sheet: 14 × 18.1 cm; pictorial area: 8.6 × 13.6 cm.
Signed in pen and dark brown ink below the pictorial area, left: 'Edw.ᵈ Dayes.', and inscribed in a different hand(?) in pencil, *verso*: 'Ullswater, Westmorland'

WITT COLLECTION 4535

The drawing, whose freshness is probably attributable to Dayes' refusal to experiment with new paints and techniques (*cf.* J. Davis, *Edward Dayes 1763–1804*, 'Old Water-Colour Society Club', Vol. XXXIX, 1964, p.54), is one of many Lakeland subjects this artist executed from *c.*1790 to his death. His first Lake District scene – *Keswick Lake* – was exhibited at the Royal Academy in 1791 (Iolo Williams, *Early English Watercolours* . . ., 1954, republished Bath, 1970, p. 98).

The small scale of the present sheet is exceptional (most of the Lakeland subjects measure approximately 25 × 45 cm: *cf.* those sold at Christie's, 13 December 1979, Lot no. 38; 3 March 1970, Lot no. 8; 6 June 1972, Lot no. 35; 8 June 1976, Lot no. 80), and may have been partly influenced, particularly in view of the decorative nature of the design, by Dayes' activities as book-illustrator.

PLATE I

Bellini *The Nativity* cat. no. 1

PLATE II

Dürer *The Emperors Charlemagne and Sigismund* cat. no. 2

PLATE III

Guercino *Aurora* cat. no. 45

PLATE IV

Rembrandt *A Quack addressing a Crowd at a Fair* cat. no. 54

PLATE V

Watteau *A Faun* cat. no. 76

PLATE VI

Tiepolo *The Holy Family with S. Joseph Reading* cat. no. 72

PLATE VII

Turner *The Crook of Lune* cat. no. 124

PLATE VIII

Cézanne *La Montagne Sainte-Victoire* cat. no. 100

The view is identical to that depicted in Dayes' *An Angler on Ullswater* (25 × 39.5 cm), sold at Christie's, 8 June 1976 (see above), except that in the Witt drawing the lightly wooded foreground bank is extended completely across the sheet.

Thomas Gainsborough *(1727–88)*

86 *A Road through a Wood, with Figures on Horseback and on foot*

Black chalk; brown and grey ink, with drawing with the point of the brush; heightening with white oil paint; yellow varnish; on pale buff laid paper. 22.1 × 30.5 cm.
Numbered by the artist(?) in pencil, *verso:* '1'.

WITT COLLECTION 1681

The drawing, which dates from the mid-1780s (John Hayes, *The Drawings of Thomas Gainsborough*, London, 1970, no. 724), was the subject, with variations, of an aquatint published by J. & J. Boydell in 1797, as no. 12 of a series of 12 (Hayes, *op. cit.*, 1971, no. 73). The drawing clearly shows Gainsborough's fascination with media and materials and technical experiment, which resulted in an overlapping of the practices of drawing and painting in his later career.

Thomas Gainsborough *(1727–88)*

87 *Wooded Landscape with Figures, Donkeys and a Cottage*

Graphite; on off-white (now unevenly discoloured and stained) laid paper. The sheet unevenly trimmed at the top, bottom and left side. 21.8 × 28.8 cm.
Inscribed in pen and brown ink, *verso:* 'Jos. Baldreys given Me Dec.ʳ 1776 by J:K: Sen.ʳ Gent'.

WITT COLLECTION 2369

This drawing, at one time identified as a study for the painting *Great Cornard Wood*, is an independent work, dated by John Hayes (no. 131) to the early to mid-1750s. It is related, in tightness of handling and in the repetitive curves of the branches of the tree, to the *Wooded landscape with Herdsmen, Cattle and Farm Building* in the Pierpont Morgan Library (Hayes no. 128).

The inscription on the verso, unknown to Hayes (*ibid.*), sheds new light on the sheet's provenance.

Thomas Gainsborough *(1727–88)*

88 *Wooded Landscape with Peasants, Donkey and Cottage*

Pencil; on pale cream (now unevenly discoloured and stained) laid paper. The sheet unevenly trimmed on all sides to a ruled line in pencil. Sheet: 30.5 × 38.8 cm; pictorial area: 28.2 × 38.8 cm.
Signed in pencil in the margin below the pictorial area, left of centre: 'Gainsborough fec. 1759', and numbered by the artist, right: '1'.

GIFT OF JOHN S. NEWBERY, 1965

This drawing, which was probably executed in Ipswich, is one of two dated sheets from 1759. The other, a *Wooded Mountain Landscape with Herdsman and Cows crossing a Bridge over a Stream*, is in the collection of Desmond J. Morris, Malta (Hayes, *op. cit.*, 1970, no. 243). Both sheets combine breadth of treatment with precise drawing of detail, which, together with the artist's clear signature, and numbering in the margin below the present sheet, indicates that they were intended as preliminary drawings for a projected series of prints, not carried out (*cf.* Hayes, *op. cit.*, no. 238 and index, erroneously listed as a Witt drawing).

Thomas Gainsborough *(1727–88)*

89 *Wooded Landscape with a Herdsman driving Cattle over a Bridge, Peasants and a Ruined Castle*

Black ink, with extensive drawing with the brush; black chalk, heightened with white chalk; on pale buff (now stained) laid paper. The sheet unevenly trimmed to an oval, and laid down twice. *Maxima*: 28.5 × 35.1 cm.

WITT COLLECTION 4181

The drawing (Hayes, *op. cit.*, no. 498) is a study for the oval oil painting exhibited at the Royal Academy in 1781 (ex-collection C.M. Michaelis: Ellis Waterhouse, *Gainsborough*, London, 1958, no. 959), and is also closely related to a soft-ground etching published by J. & J. Boydell in 1797 (John Hayes, *Gainsborough as Printmaker*, London, 1971, no. 66). Hayes (1971, *ibid.*) suggests that the present sheet marks an intermediary stage between the detailed etching, and the more abstract and rhythmical painting: indeed, the figures to the left of the bridge in the etching, identifiable as rustic lovers, are in the Witt drawing generalised to the extent that their sex and relationship is irrelevant.

Thomas Girtin *(1775–1802)*

90 *Farmyard landscape with Barns, Ladder and Figures*

Soft pencil; brown ink, and restricted watercolour washes, with some drawing with the point of the brush; pink and yellow bodycolour; drawing of detail in pen and the point of the brush in brown ink; on pale buff laid paper. The sheet unevenly trimmed at all sides. 23 × 29 cm.
Signed in brush(?) and brown ink, bottom left of centre: 'Girtin 1800'
Verso: A Sky (unfinished), watercolour.

SPOONER COLLECTION 42

The drawing, although accepted by Girtin and Loshak (*op. cit.*, no. 408) as a work of 1800 (*cf.* also Francis Hawcroft, *op. cit.*, no. 78, who confuses dates), is thought by them to be a reversion to the style Girtin used *c.* 1798, when under the influence of Canaletto's dot-and-dash style of drawing. The unfinished drawing of a sky on the *verso* was discovered when the sheet was removed from its mount in 1979.

Thomas Girtin *(1775–1802)*

91 *Appledore, W. Devon*

Pencil; pen and brown ink, restricted watercolour washes, with drawing with the pen and point of the brush; white and other coloured bodycolour; on pale buff laid paper. The sheet unevenly trimmed at all sides. 24 × 47 cm.
Signed in pen and dark grey ink, bottom left: 'Girtin'.

WITT COLLECTION 846

This panoramic drawing (Thomas Girtin and David Loshack, *The Art of Thomas Girtin*, London, 1954, no. 254), remarkable for its interpretation of limpid atmosphere and reflection, is probably a studio work based on sketches Girtin did during his tour of the south-west in 1797, and can thus be dated to the following year. Francis Hawcroft (*Watercolours by Thomas Girtin*, Whitworth Art Gallery, Manchester and Victoria & Albert Museum, London, 1975, no. 36) has noted the drawing's relationship with other coastal views by Girtin of the same period.

The view shown in this drawing is taken from Instow sands looking west across the estuary of the river Torridge.

Paul Sandby *(1725–1809)*

92 *Miss Marsden*

Red chalk, with use of rubbing or the stump, heightened with white chalk applied with the brush; on pale cream (now stained and unevenly discoloured) laid paper, prepared by the artist with a ground of very dilute brown (ink?) wash. The sheet unevenly trimmed at all sides, the bottom right corner torn away. 24.3 × 16 cm.
Inscribed by the artist(?) in pencil, bottom centre: 'Miss Marsden', and in a later hand: 'F', and: 'F.H'. Inscribed in a modern hand in pencil, *verso:* 'F. Hayman R A'.

WITT COLLECTION 1130

The identity of Miss Marsden is unknown, but she may have been one of the more eminent local figures in Windsor. A larger (25.3 × 16.3 cm) and more elaborate drawing in red, black and white chalk of the same figure with a landscape background, is at Windsor (A.P. Oppé, *Sandby Drawings at Windsor Castle*, London, 1947, no. 272). Although Miss Marsden is more finely dressed in the Windsor drawing, she wears the hat with hanging ribbon visible in the present sheet.

Both Windsor and Witt sheets are inscribed by the same hand with the name of the sitter, both have the 'F' mark, and both are inscribed with the forged initials of Francis Hayman.

Paul Sandby *(1725–1809)*

93 *The Henry VIII Gateway, Windsor*

Pencil, grey watercolour wash; extensive use of white and other coloured bodycolour; some scraping and retinting on left side of arch and on tower; extensive drawing of detail with pen and point of the brush in grey and brown wash, both freehand and ruled; touches of gold paint; on white wove paper. The drawing enclosed within ruled lines in pen and brown and grey wash. The sheet unevenly trimmed at all sides, and laid down on the artist's mount. 37 × 47.1 cm.
Signed in brush and gold paint, bottom left: 'P Sandby Pinx^t 1767', and inscribed by the artist on the notice on the left of the tower: 'WINDSOR/and/EATON. MACH/Sold (?) out', and on the notice on the right of the tower: 'Pray Remember/the Poor Confin'd/Debtors'
Inscribed in a different hand in pencil, on the back of the mount: The Town Gate & Debtor's Prison/Windsor Castle/P. Sandby 1767'

SPOONER COLLECTION 84

Two drawings related to this work are at Windsor (A.P. Oppé, *Sandby Drawings at Windsor Castle*, London, 1947, nos. 27, 28), which Oppé, to whom the Spooner drawing was unknown, regarded as the preliminary sketch and finished work, respectively. Although the Spooner sheet includes elements from both Windsor drawings, in composition and general placing of the figures, it follows Oppé no. 27 most closely. A drawing of a related subject, a view of *Henry VIII Gateway from Without*, also at Windsor (Oppé no. 26), may also be assigned to a similar date to that of the Spooner sheet.

Francis Towne *(c.1740–1816)*

94 *The Forest of Radnor, with the Black Mountains in the distance*

Traces of pencil; contour drawing in pen and grey ink wash; black ink wash, and restricted watercolour washes, with some drawing with the point of the brush; re-drawing of foreground detail with pen and the point of the brush in dark grey ink; on off-white wove paper. The drawing made up of two sheets, trimmed at the edges and laid down.
17.2 × 50.6 cm.
Inscribed by the artist in pen and brown ink, *verso* of right sheet: 'The Forest of Radnor the blackmountains in the lefthand distance', and numbered on the *versos* of both sheets: '3 & 4'

SPOONER COLLECTION 90

See cat. no. 95.

Francis Towne *(c.1740–1816)*

95 *Near Devil's Bridge, Central Wales*

Traces of pencil; contour-drawing in pen and grey ink; black and brown ink washes, and restricted watercolour washes, with some drawing with the point of the brush; orange bodycolour; on off-white wove paper. The drawing made up of two sheets, trimmed at the edges and laid down.
17.1 × 51.3 cm.
Inscribed by the artist in pen and brown ink, *verso* of right sheet: 'near the Devils Bridge', and: 'Join', and in pencil on the *verso* of the left sheet: 'Join'. Numbered in pencil on the *verso* of the right sheet: '1 & 2'.

SPOONER COLLECTION 91

This and the previous drawing were published by Philip Troutman (*The Evocation of Atmosphere in the English Watercolour*, Apollo, July 1968, p. 55) as works dating from Towne's Welsh tour of 1777, although the intense blues of the sky and touches of bodycolour would indicate a later date. There is evidence of a Welsh tour of 1810 (*Devil's Bridge* (16.8 × 24.7 cm) dated 1810, and a view near Devil's Bridge (25.5 × 17.2 cm) dated 25 August 1810, both with the Fine Art Society), and it is likely, in view of the watermarked date of 1808 on the Spooner sheets, that they too were products of the same tour. As Troutman (*ibid.*) noted, the drawings were probably intended as a pair, and while the numbering on the *versos* confirms this, it may also indicate the possibility of there being further Welsh drawings of the same format.

Richard Wilson *(1714–82)*

96 *The Thames looking towards Syon House*

Pencil; black chalk, with extensive use of the stump and rubbing; heightened with white chalk; touches of red chalk; on grey laid paper. The sheet unevenly trimmed at all sides, and tears repaired bottom, right, and bottom left corner.
32.4 × 52.7 cm.
Collector's mark: Earl of Warwick.

SPOONER COLLECTION 102

This highly finished drawing is unrecorded by both Brinsley Ford (*The Drawings of Richard Wilson*, London, 1951) and W.G. Constable (*Richard Wilson*, London 1953). Although the subject includes Syon House (identifiable on the distant right bank), the drawing is unconnected with the two painted versions of *Syon House from Richmond Gardens* (Constable, *op. cit.* 54 a and b). Compositionally, the wide expanse of water and the placing of the foreground figures suggests a connection with the drawing of *Wilton House viewed from the South-East* (Constable no. 58 a).

61

62

63

64

65

66

67

68

69

70

71

72

73

74

75

76

77

78

79

80

81

82

83

84

85

86

87

88

89

90

91

92

Miss Marsden

93

94

94

95

96

The Nineteenth Century

Paul Cézanne *(1839–1906)*

97 *An Armchair*

Pencil and watercolour. 32.2 × 33.8 cm.
Faint and illegible inscription, bottom left.

PRINCES GATE COLLECTION 238

This watercolour probably dates from *c.*1885–90; of about the same date there is a pencil study by Cézanne (Koerfer Collection, Switzerland) showing apparently the same chair with a cushion. The subject suggests comparison with van Gogh's *Chair* (National Gallery) of 1888. (Princes Gate Catalogue 132)

Paul Cézanne *(1839–1906)*

98 *A Garden Shed*

Soft pencil; watercolour, with drawing with the point of the brush; on off-white wove paper. The sheet unevenly trimmed at the bottom. 31.4 × 47.5 cm.
Inscribed in pencil, *verso:* 'X Vold' (?), and numbered in blue crayon: '66'.

COURTAULD COLLECTION 21

The drawing has been dated by Lionello Venturi (*Cézanne : Son Art – Son Oeuvre,* Paris, 1936, no 837) to 1872–77, and by Robert Ratcliffe (*Watercolour and Pencil Drawings by Cézanne,* Laing Art Gallery, Newcastle-upon-Tyne, and Hayward Gallery, London, 1973, no. 42) to *c.*1880.

This comparatively early watercolour shares with the drawings of *Little Houses* and two versions of *Entrance to a Garden* (Venturi, nos. 836, 840 and 842, respectively) a detailed and regularly hatched under-drawing, a composition in which solidly constructed, predominantly rectilinear forms are contrasted with the slow curves of foliage, and an interest in the domestic and intimate.

Paul Cézanne *(1839–1906)*

99 *Madame Cézanne Sewing*

Pencil. Laid down. 47.3 × 31 cm.

PRINCES GATE COLLECTION 239

Cézanne met Hortense Fiquet in 1869 and began living with her in the following year; they married in 1886. Of the numerous pencil studies of the artist's wife few are so complete or finished as this, which has been dated either to the years immediately after or to some years before their marriage. (Princes Gate Catalogue 133)

Paul Cézanne *(1839–1906)*

100 *La Montagne Sainte-Victoire*
COLOUR PLATE VIII

Drawing with soft pencil, apparently under and over the painted areas; watercolour or very dilute gouache, with extensive drawing with the point and flat of the brush (mixing slightly with the pencil in certain areas); on off-white (now stained) laid paper. The sheet unevenly torn along the bottom, and in part torn away at the left side. All other sides uneven. 32.8 × 50.5 cm.

COURTAULD COLLECTION 22

The drawing has been dated by Venturi (*op. cit.*, no. 1023) to 1890–1900, although Ratcliffe (*op. cit.*, no. 55) has assigned to it the date of 1885–7, the period during which Cézanne painted a similar view of the mountain in oil (Courtauld Coll., Venturi 454). Both oil and watercolour views are taken from roughly due West (Ratcliffe, p. 162).

Paul Cézanne *(1839–1906)*

101 *A Statue under Trees*

Pencil and watercolour. 48.1 × 31.3 cm.

A late work, of the second half of the 1890s, this drawing is comparable with a number of other watercolours of the same dimensions done at the Château Noir. (Princes Gate Catalogue 157)

Paul Cézanne *(1839–1906)*

102 *Still-life with Apples, Bottle and Chairback*

Pencil, both under and over painted areas; gouache(?), with extensive drawing with the brush; on white wove paper. The sheet unevenly torn, right, apparently to ruled lines in pencil, and torn at the bottom. 45.8 × 60.4 cm.

Venturi (*op. cit.*, no. 1155) dates this painterly watercolour to 1904–6. Robert Ratcliffe (*op. cit.*, no. 98) has given a wider dating of 1902–6, endorsed by John Rewald (*Cézanne. The Late Work*, Museum of Modern Art, New York, 1977, no. 77).

As Ratcliffe (*ibid.*) has observed, the boldly brushed-in chairback has close affinities with the drawing *The Rococo Clock* (Adrien Chappuis, *The Drawings of Paul Cézanne*, Greenwich, Conn. and London, 1973, no. 1223). It is also reminiscent of the chairback in the watercolour in the collection of Lord Clark of Saltwood (Venturi, *op. cit.*, no. 850). The paint employed in this work is, in certain areas, opaque, and sufficiently dense to form ridges at the edge of the brush-stroke.

Honoré Daumier *(1808–79)*

103 *The Hypochondriac*

Traces of black chalk; black ink and restricted watercolour washes, with drawing with the pen and point of the brush; lithographic(?) crayon; on off-white (now stained) laid paper. The sheet unevenly trimmed at all sides. 20.7 × 27.1 cm. Signed in pen and black ink, lower left: 'h.', and below: 'h. Daumier' (over a previous signature in grey wash). Numbered by a later hand in pencil, *verso*: '6403'

Drawings by Daumier are never dated, and only a few can be reliably dated because of their connection with lithographs or paintings. The Courtauld sheet may be tentatively dated to *c.*1857, because of its relationship with a drawing of a similar subject, now lost, presumed destroyed in the Second World War (*cf.* K.E. Maison, *Honoré Daumier: catalogue raisonné of the paintings, watercolours and drawings*, Vol. II, London, 1968, no. 486), and with the lithograph, *Trente deux degrés (cf.* Jean Adhémar, *Honoré Daumier, Drawings and Watercolours*, Basle, 1954, p. 35).

Honoré Daumier *(1808–99)*

104 *The Defence*

Touches of pencil; pen and grey ink, and brush and grey ink wash; pen and black ink; on white (now discoloured) wove paper. The left side of the sheet unevenly torn, all other sides unevenly trimmed. Vestiges of lines in pen and black ink at all edges of the sheet. 23.7 × 31.5 cm. Signed in pencil, lower right: 'h.D.' Numbered in different hands in pencil, *verso*: '2a–81'

The drawing is almost identical, with the exception of the wash, to an unsigned sheet in a German private collection (Maison, *op. cit.*, no. 656; the Courtauld drawing no. 657). Both works are equally freely drawn, both show various *pentimenti*, and it is impossible to determine which version preceded the other.

Edgar Degas *(1834–1917)*

105 *A Woman adjusting her Hair*

Black chalk and pastel, with use of rubbing; on buff wove paper. The drawing made up of two sheets and laid down. Sight measurements: 62 × 59 cm. Stamped in red, bottom right: 'Degas' (from the II Vente Degas, Paris, 11 December 1918)

COURTAULD COLLECTION 36

This pastel, of *c*.1884, is considered by Lemoisne (*Degas et son oeuvre*, Paris, 1946, Vol. III, no. 781) to be a preliminary study for the oil painting of the same subject, formerly in the collection of Georges Viau (Lemoisne, 780), and is a re-working of the theme of the pastel *At the Milliner's* of the previous year (Lemoisne, 729).

The woman at the left of the earlier pastel has affinities with her counterpart in the Viau painting: both figures are placed almost parallel to the picture plane, both heads are in the same pose, and cropped at the top in a similar manner, and both are drawn with similarly relaxed contours. While the figure in the Courtauld drawing is in roughly the same pose as the woman in the painting, and is certainly more closely related than the woman in the 1883 pastel, there are important differences. She is drawn from a higher viewpoint, her face is turned away from the spectator, the top of the head is not cropped, her left arm is raised higher (see the *pentimenti*) and she leans forward, forming a silhouette of greater dynamism than the figure in the oil. Given these differences, and the relationship of the figure in the Viau oil with that of the pastel of 1883, it could be suggested that the Courtauld drawing is not a preliminary study for the oil, but is a work executed concurrently, or possibly after it.

Eugène Delacroix *(1798–1863)*

106 *A Moroccan Jewess*

Watercolour over faint traces of pencil. 26.8 × 19.6 cm.
Dated by the artist, bottom centre: '19 Aout 47'; numerals inscribed on *recto* (top right) and *verso*, where are also recent pencil notes.

PRINCES GATE COLLECTION 419

In 1832 Delacroix visited Morocco where he made numerous watercolours, including studies of a Jewish wedding and of Jewish women in their homes. Years later he was still painting reminiscences of these experiences, including five paintings of Moroccan subjects in 1847, the year of this watercolour.

Eugène Delacroix *(1798–1863)*

107 *Two Branches with Leaves*

Pencil and watercolour. 25.3 × 39.3 cm.
Dated in pencil by the artist, bottom left: 'Champrosay 28 oct. 60'. Collector's mark: Delacroix Sale.

PRINCES GATE COLLECTION 235

Delacroix rented a house at Champrosay, near the forest of Sénart, in 1844; he later bought it and often stayed there in retirement. At the time of this watercolour he was travelling almost daily to Saint-Sulpice, working on the final stages of his mural decorations. (Princes Gate Catalogue 160)

Vincent Van Gogh *(1853–90)*

108 *The Tile Factory*

Pencil; pen and brown ink; on very pale buff (now stained) wove paper. The sheet, unevenly trimmed at the left.
25.6 × 34.8 cm.
Numbered by the artist(?) in pen and brown ink, *verso*: '174'.

COURTAULD COLLECTION 177

Jan Hulsker (*The complete Van Gogh*, New York, 1977, no. 1373) has dated this drawing to March 1888, noting its similarity of scale with the drawing *A Path through a Field with Willows* (Van Gogh Museum, Amsterdam: Hulsker 1372), dated by the artist to the March of that year.

The Courtauld sheet, which may have been taken from a sketch-book (the uneven trimming at the left of the sheet may indicate that the book's spine was at the left) has deep impressions of diagonal hatchings across its centre, probably transferred from the sheet above, which may have been the Amsterdam drawing.

Edouard Manet *(1832–83)*

109 *Seated Nude*

Red chalk; on white (now stained) laid paper. The sheet unevenly trimmed at all sides, and pressed through for engraving. 29 × 20.8 cm.

COURTAULD COLLECTION 85

The theme and composition of bather and maid may have been partly suggested by a pencil drawing Manet made between 1852 and 1858, recording figures in Andrea del Sarto's *Baptism of the People* (Scalzo, Florence) (Alain de Leiris, *The Drawings of Edouard Manet*, Berkeley and Los Angeles, 1969, no. 58).

Thematically, the Courtauld drawing, which appears to have been executed specifically for translation into an etching, is related to the group of four paintings *The Surprised Nymph* of 1861 (Paul Jamot and Georges Wildenstein, *Manet*, Paris, 1932, nos. 53, 54, 55, and a painting of the same subject formerly in the Lamentron Collection, Paris, omitted by Jamot and Wildenstein). The etching of this subject, in reverse, was published in 1862 (*cf.* Juliet Wilson, *Edouard Manet: l'oeuvre gravé*, Ingelheim-am-Rhein, 1977, no. 8).

Auguste Rodin *(1840–1917)*

110 *Female Nude reclining on her Back*

Pencil, with some rubbing; restricted watercolour washes, with drawing with the flat and point of the brush; on off-white wove paper, given a very dilute orange watercolour ground. The drawing unevenly stained. All edges of the sheet uneven. 27.5 × 36.3 cm.
Signed in pencil, lower right of centre: 'A Rodin', and numbered in a different hand, *verso:* 'XI/M.M.C.C.'

COURTAULD COLLECTION 128

The drawing has been dated by Douglas Cooper to after 1900. It is related in pose and in feeling for the mass of the figure to the *Nude on her Back, with hanging Arm and raised Leg* (29.5 × 37 cm) sold at the Galeries Georges Petit (Troisième Vente), Paris, 27–28 October 1933 (no. 96).

Georges Seurat *(1859–91)*

111 *Standing Female Nude*

Drawing with the stump impregnated with pencil; black (Conté?) crayon; slight scraping; on off-white laid paper. The sheet irregular. 63.2 × 48.2 cm.
Inscribed in pencil, verso: 'de Georges Seurat/felF', and numbered in red crayon: '381'.

COURTAULD COLLECTION 140 (not catalogued by Douglas Cooper)

R.L. Herbert (*Seurat's Drawings*, London, 1962, no. 23) was the first author to attribute this ambitious drawing to Seurat, dating it to *c.*1879, and relating it to a preliminary line drawing in an unknown collection (Herbert, no. 22). That the drawing is a genuine work by Seurat appears to be confirmed by the inscription on the *verso*, apparently in Félix Fénéon's hand.

The connection with Fantin-Latour's lithographs – the use of dense blacks, and the choice of buxom model – is clear, as is Seurat's Beaux-Arts training, manifest by the continued use of the stump (in the breast, lower abdomen and shadow on the leg), and in the tendency, noticeable through a comparison with the preliminary sketch, to idealise the figure.

Henri de Toulouse-Lautrec *(1864–1901)*

112 *A Woman lying in Bed*

Soft pencil; touches of grey watercolour wash in the head; on off-white (now discoloured) laid paper. The sheet trimmed at the bottom, all other edges uneven. 30.3 × 48 cm.
Signed in pencil, lower left: 'H T-Lautrec' (the initials in monogram), and inscribed in a different hand, *verso:* 'M.r Claude Sayle', with dimensions.

COURTAULD COLLECTION 161

The drawing, dated by Douglas Cooper (*The Courtauld Collection*, London 1954, no. 154) to *c.*1896, has a similar tenderness and quietness of mood to the oil painting *Woman seated in Bed* (55 × 46 cm.) of 1877 (Private Collection, France).

John Constable *(1776–1837)*

113 *Willy Lott's Cottage viewed from the East*

Pencil; on white (now unevenly discoloured and stained) wove paper. The drawing made up of three sheets, the central sheet unevenly trimmed to a ruled line in pencil, right, and roughly torn at the left. The right side of the drawing unevenly trimmed. 19.9 × 28.4 cm.

WITT COLLECTION 1505

The sheet has been dated by Leslie Parris, Ian Fleming-Williams and Conal Shields (*Constable Paintings, Watercolours & Drawings*, Tate Gallery, 1976, no. 115) to 1812 (for the central sheet) and 1813 for the addition at either side. The drawing is the first to show Willy Lott's house as the centre of a composition, and is closely related to the painting of 1835, *The Valley Farm* (Tate Gallery).

John Constable *(1776–1837)*

114 *East Bergholt Church*

Hard and soft pencil, with use of the ruler; on off-white (now unevenly discoloured) wove paper. The sheet unevenly trimmed at all sides, apparently to a ruled line in pencil. 31.7 × 23.8 cm.

SPOONER COLLECTION 16

The drawing has been dated to 1817 by Parris, Fleming-Williams and Shields (*op. cit.*, no. 155) who suggest that it may have been exhibited at the Royal Academy, 1818 (no. 446), under the title of *A Gothic Porch*, and as such, would have been a pendant to the equally impressive pencil drawing of *Elm Trees in old Park, East Bergholt* (Graham Reynolds, *op. cit.*, no. 162) also exhibited that year.

John Constable *(1776–1837)*

115 *Colliers off the Beach at Brighton*

Pencil; on white (now unevenly stained and discoloured) laid paper. The sheet unevenly trimmed at all sides. 11.6 × 18.6 cm. Dated by the artist in pencil, bottom left: 'Brighton / friday 14 oct. 1825'

WITT COLLECTION 2541M

An almost identical view is shown in the small oil on paper sketch, dated 17 July 1824, in the Victoria and Albert Museum (*cf.* Graham Reynolds, *Catalogue of the Constable Collection, Victoria and Albert Museum*, London, 1973, no. 266)

Henry (Johann Heinrich) Fuseli *(1741–1825)*

116 *Titania's Dream*

Pencil, with use of rubbing; black ink, and restricted watercolour washes, with drawing with the brush, and use of the dry brush; on pale buff (now stained) laid paper. The sheet unevenly trimmed at all sides to a ruled line in pencil, and laid down. 38 × 38.1 cm.
Dated by the artist in brush and grey wash, right: 'l (?) May 22'.

WITT COLLECTION 2841

The drawing, regarded by Nicolas Powell (*The Drawings of Henry Fuseli*, London, 1951, no. 61) as one of Fuseli's latest extant drawings, has been assigned the date of 1790–1800 by Gert Schiff (*Johan Heinrich Füssli 1741–1825*, Zürich and Munich, 1973, no. 1080), who suggests that the date should read as 'May 22', the stroke before 'May' having been made in error. The drawing is a highly worked study for the painting in the collection of E.M. Sandoz, Château de Burier, France (Schiff no. 923), in which the major changes are the re-drawing of Titania's head and breast. The initial idea for Titania's pose is to be found on a sheet of figure studies datable to *c.*1790 in the collection of Armide Oppé (Schiff no. 1054).

Henry (Johann Heinrich) Fuseli
(1741–1825)

117 *Rear view of a Standing Woman*

Pencil; black ink and restricted watercolour wash, with drawing with the brush; white and other coloured bodycolour in the coiffeur; on off-white (now discoloured and stained) laid paper. The sheet unevenly trimmed at all sides, apparently to a ruled line in pencil. 48 × 30.3 cm. Numbered in a modern hand in pencil, *verso*: '#1' Collector's mark: Baroness North (*verso*)

WITT COLLECTION 3937

The drawing has been dated by Schiff (*op. cit.*, no. 1068) to 1796–1800, and is one of three drawings, all executed at approximately the same time, concentrating on women viewed from the rear, and exaggerating the roundness and solidity of form of the neck, arms and back. Almost a pendant to the Witt drawing, although handled with a broken, less rhythmical contour, is the *Two Woman Walking* in Belfast Museum and Art Gallery (Schiff no. 1067). The third drawing, *A Woman seated at a Spinet*, is in the Witt Collection (3092, Courtauld Institute Galleries).

The right arm of the woman in the present sheet is reminiscent of Fuseli's illustration of the arm for J.C. Lavater's *Essays on Physiognomy*, engraved by Thomas Holloway and published in 1792 (*cf*. Schiff no. 971).

John Frederick Lewis *(1805–76)*

118 *A Street Scene in Cairo – The Street and Mosque of the Ghoreyah*

Pencil, with rubbing and extensive use of the stump, and with the use of the ruler in the architecture; watercolour, with some drawing with the point of the brush; red, orange, yellow, ochre and blue body-colour; white chalk brushed on in all areas, and mixing with the watercolour and body-colour; on pale buff wove paper. The sheet trimmed at all sides, a tear repaired bottom right of centre, and laid down. 37.5 × 54 cm.

WITT COLLECTION 3051

The drawing is one of six views of this location recorded by Michael Lewis (*John Frederick Lewis*, Leigh-on-Sea, 1978, nos. 511–17 inclusive: the Witt drawing is recorded twice under different titles and dimensions, as nos. 511 and 515), to which may be added an unfinished oil-painting (113 × 86.5 cm) signed and dated 1876, which was sold at Christie's, Central Hotel, Glasgow, 2 and 3 April 1969, Lot no. 23, and is now in a private collection in America (*cf. John Frederick Lewis, R.A.* Laing Art Gallery, Newcastle-upon-Tyne, 1971, no. 59). This is probably the painting exhibited posthumously at the Royal Academy in 1877 (no. 454).

The oil painting, and a smaller version in oil and watercolour in the Forbes Magazine Collection (identifiable as Lewis 516) are related to the present drawing only in that they share details of the background. The Witt sheet, which records on a vast scale and with equal impartiality architecture and characters, cannot properly be regarded as a study for either painting, in which dramatically presented foreground figures and narrative incident predominate.

Samuel Palmer *(1805–81)*

119 *Trefriew Mill, on the Road from Bettwys y Coed to Conway, North Wales*

Soft pencil or black chalk; brown ink and restricted watercolour washes; white and other coloured bodycolour; drawing of detail with the point of the brush in watercolour and brown and black ink; over-drawing with soft pencil or black chalk; on pale buff (now discoloured) wove paper. Vestiges of a ruled line in black chalk on the left and right sides of the sheet. The bottom of the sheet irregular. 40.1 × 48.6 cm.
Inscribed by the artist in pen and brown ink, lower left: 'Trefriew Mill on the Road from Bettws y Coed to Conway N.Wales/Samuel Palmer 4 Grove Street Lisson Grove Marylebone', and dated below: '1835', and inscribed in pencil below the date: 'at Trefriew NW', and numbered bottom right: '12'.

SPOONER COLLECTION 68

This highly finished drawing, executed in London (*cf.* inscriptions) but probably worked up from notes and sketches, is a product of Palmer's tour of Wales, made in the company of Henry Walter and Edward Calvert during the August of 1835.

The Welsh tour was a disappointment to Palmer: he wrote to George Richmond from Tintern on 19 and 20 August complaining of the expense he had incurred ('Had I conceived how much it would cost I would have soon have started for the United States as Wales . . .': (Raymond Lister (ed.), *The Letters of Samuel Palmer*, 1974, Vol. 1)); of the (for him) uncongenial weather ('. . . near Snowdon we had white light days on which we could count the stubbs and stones some miles off . . .': Lister, *ibid.*); and of his laziness ('. . . I have not worked hard . . .': Lister, *ibid.*).

It would seem that the Spooner drawing was made probably in late September 1835, in a burst of energy possibly stimulated partly by Palmer's association with Hannah Linnell (Lister, *op. cit.*, letter, 18 September 1835 to John Linnell), and partly by his worsening financial state.

Joseph Mallord William Turner
(1775–1851)

120 *Chepstow Castle*

Pencil; restricted watercolour washes, with extensive drawing with the point of the brush, and in part, pen; on white laid paper. The sheet trimmed at all sides, apparently to a ruled line in pencil. 21 × 30 cm.
Signed in brush and grey wash, bottom left: 'Turner' (the 'e' a large cursive).

STEPHEN COURTAULD COLLECTION 1

The drawing was published in the *Copper-Plate Magazine*, 1 November 1794.

For a more detailed discussion of this drawing see Michael Kitson, *Turner Watercolours from the Collection of Stephen Courtauld*, Courtauld Institute Galleries, 1974, no. 1, and William Bradford and Philip Troutman, *Turner Prout Steer*, Courtauld Institute Galleries, 1980, p. 1, no. 1.

Joseph Mallord William Turner
(1775–1851)

121 *The Falls of the Rhine at Schaffhausen*

Touches of pencil; watercolour; white bodycolour; scraping out; red ink, applied with pen and the point of the brush; on off-white laid paper. The drawing edged by a ruled line in black ink. The sheet unevenly trimmed at the left edge. 23.3 × 29.6 cm.
Verso: A Two Masted Sailing Vessel, Sailing Barge and Rowing Boats, in pencil.

STEPHEN COURTAULD COLLECTION 9

The removal of the backing in 1980 revealed the slight sketch on the *verso* (*cf.* Kitson, *op. cit.*, no. 9, and Bradford and Troutman, *op. cit.*, p. 6, no. 10). A work of Turner's late period.

Joseph Mallord William Turner
(1775–1851)

122 *Dawn after the Wreck*

Pencil; watercolour, with drawing with point of the brush; white and other coloured bodycolour; touches of red chalk; rubbing and retinting; on white laid paper. The drawing edged with a ruled line in pen and brown ink. 25.2 × 38 cm.

STEPHEN COURTAULD COLLECTION 11

The preliminary drawing in pencil in the foreground, left of centre, suggesting the receding posts of a breakwater and flotsam from a wreck indicates an earlier intention not carried out.

For full discussion of this drawing, *cf.* Kitson, *op. cit.*, no. 11, and Bradford and Troutman, *op. cit.*, no. 12. A work of Turner's late period, certainly after 1830, probably 1840.

Joseph Mallord William Turner
(1775–1851)

123 *Colchester*

Traces of pencil; watercolour, with drawing with the brush and use of the dry brush; white and other coloured bodycolour; touches of white, red and other coloured chalks; scraping out, and scoring into the wet paint with the point of the brush-handle; on pale grey-green laid paper, the upper half, except for the area of the sun, given a very pale grey ground. 28.8 × 40.7 cm.

STEPHEN COURTAULD COLLECTION 8

Engraved on copper by R. Wallis for *Picturesque Views in England and Wales*, Part II, no. 1, 1827.

For a full discussion of this drawing, *cf.* Kitson, *op. cit.*, no. 8, and Bradford and Troutman, *op. cit.*, p. 5, no. 9.

Joseph Mallord William Turner
(1775–1851)

124 *The Crook of Lune* COLOUR PLATE VII

Pencil; watercolour, with drawing with the point of the brush, and use of the dry brush; touches of white and other coloured bodycolour; extensive scraping and re-tinting, and scoring into the wet paint with the point of the brush-handle; touches of gum or varnish; touches of black chalk; slight use of finger-printing; on white laid paper. 29.1 × 43 cm.

STEPHEN COURTAULD COLLECTION 6

Datable to 1816–18, and one of the designs for the *History of Richmondshire*, published by Longman's, 1819–23. *Cf.* Kitson, *op. cit.*, no. 6; *cf.* Bradford and Troutman, *op. cit.*, p. 3, no. 6.

Joseph Mallord William Turner
(1775–1851)

125 *The Drachenfels*

Touches of pencil; watercolour, with drawing with the brush, and use of the dry brush; printing with the side of the finger; white and other coloured bodycolour; some scraping out; on pale grey wove paper. 20.9 × 29 cm.

SPOONER COLLECTION 92

One of Turner's more informal watercolours, dated by Andrew Wilton (*The Life and Work of J.M.W. Turner*, London, 1979, no. 667) to the second Continental tour of 1817. For a more complete discussion of the drawing, see Bradford and Troutman, *op. cit.*, p. 4, no. 7.

Sir David Wilkie *(1785–1841)*

126 *Madame Josephine, Landlady of the Hotel, Constantinople*

Black chalk, with red chalk in the figure only; pencil, restricted to the contours of the head and collar, the hands and patterns on the sleeves and the border of the overskirt; black (Indian?) ink and blue watercolour washes (of varying strengths and combinations, and mixing in certain areas (i.e. the window, cushions and overskirt) with the chalks to form bodycolour); white, red, yellow and pale blue bodycolour (mixing with the graphite and chalks in certain areas), with extensive drawing with the point of the brush; on buff tinted (now unevenly stained) wove paper. 47.2 × 33.1 cm. Inscribed by the artist in pen and brown ink, bottom, right of centre: 'D Wilkie f. Constantinople October 1840'.

SPOONER COLLECTION 101

This late drawing, with its clear references to Rubens in the handling of coloured chalks, was the subject of a lithograph of 1843 by Joseph Nash (as *Madame Josephine, the Land Lady of the Hotel, Constantinople: in a Turkish Dress*) reproduced in *Sketches in Turkey, 1840–1, XXIV*.

97

98

99

100

101

102

103

104

105

106

107

108

109

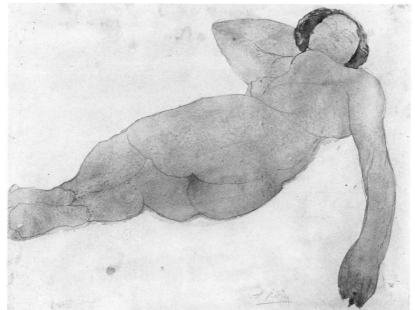

110

111

112

113

114

115

116

117

118

119

120

121

122

123

124

125

126

Index of Artists